SCOTT FORESMAN · ADDISON WESLEY

Mathematics

Grade 2

Answer Key for Homework Workbook

PEARSON

Scott
Foresman

Editorial Offices: Glenview, Illinois • Parsippany, New Jersey • New York, New York

Sales Offices: Parsippany, New Jersey • Duluth, Georgia • Glenview, Illinois
Coppell, Texas • Ontario, California • Mesa, Arizona

ISBN 0-328-07563-9

6 7 8 9 10 V011 09 08 07 06 05

Name _____

Joining Groups to Add

R 1-1

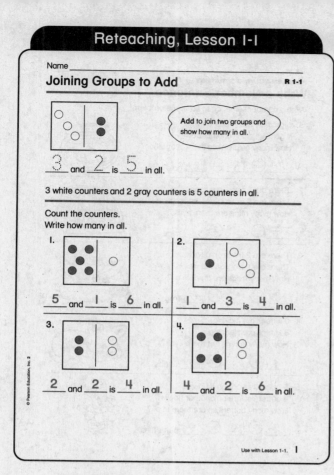

Add to join two groups and show how many in all.

__3__ and __2__ is __5__ in all.

3 white counters and 2 gray counters is 5 counters in all.

Count the counters.
Write how many in all.

1.

__5__ and __1__ is __6__ in all.

2.

__1__ and __3__ is __4__ in all.

3.

__2__ and __2__ is __4__ in all.

4.

__4__ and __2__ is __6__ in all.

© Pearson Education, Inc. 2

Use with Lesson 1-1. **1**

Name _____

Joining Groups to Add

P 1-1

Count the fruit in the two groups.
Draw and write how many there are in all.

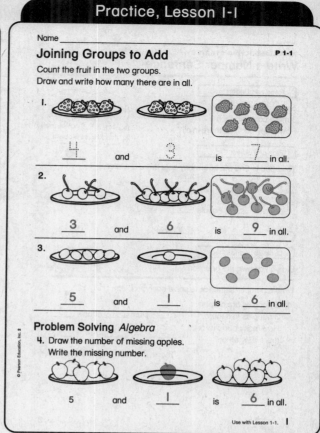

1.

__4__ and __3__ is __7__ in all.

2.

__3__ and __6__ is __9__ in all.

3.

__5__ and __1__ is __6__ in all.

Problem Solving *Algebra*

4. Draw the number of missing apples.
   Write the missing number.

5 and __1__ is __6__ in all.

© Pearson Education, Inc. 2

Use with Lesson 1-1. **1**

Name _____

Writing Addition Sentences

R 1-2

How many counters are there in all?

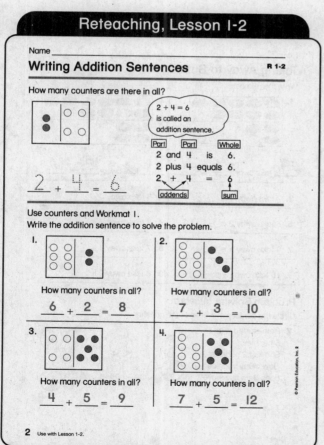

$2 + 4 = 6$ is called an addition sentence.

| Part | Part | Whole |

2 and 4 is 6.
2 plus 4 equals 6.

$2 + 4 = 6$

addends   sum

__2__ + __4__ = __6__

Use counters and Workmat 1.
Write the addition sentence to solve the problem.

1.

How many counters in all?
__6__ + __2__ = __8__

2.

How many counters in all?
__7__ + __3__ = __10__

3.

How many counters in all?
__4__ + __5__ = __9__

4.

How many counters in all?
__7__ + __5__ = __12__

© Pearson Education, Inc. 2

2 Use with Lesson 1-2.

Name _____

Writing Addition Sentences

P 1-2

Write an addition sentence to solve the problem.

1. 5 boys are at the party.
   6 girls are at the party.
   How many children are there in all?
   __5__ + __6__ = __11__ children

2. There are 6 blue hats.
   There are 2 red hats.
   How many hats are there in all?
   __6__ + __2__ = __8__ hats

3. 4 children play a game.
   5 children sing a song.
   How many children are there in all?
   __4__ + __5__ = __9__ children

4. 7 cups are on the table.
   1 cup is on a shelf.
   How many cups are there in all?
   __7__ + __1__ = __8__ cups

5. There are 3 red ribbons.
   There are 3 blue ribbons.
   How many ribbons are there in all?
   __3__ + __3__ = __6__ ribbons

6. There are 7 gifts for Suzi.
   There are 0 gifts for David.
   How many gifts are there in all?
   __7__ + __0__ = __7__ gifts

Problem Solving *Visual Thinking*

Complete the addition sentence.

7. There are 7 balloons in all.
   Color some balloons red.
   Color some balloons blue.

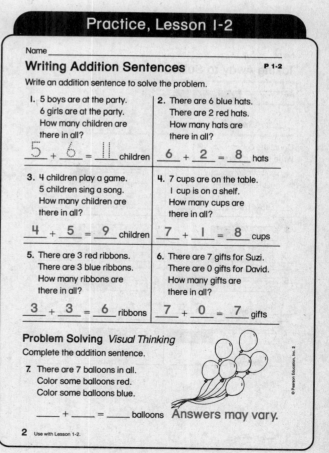

_____ + _____ = _____ balloons   Answers may vary.

© Pearson Education, Inc. 2

2 Use with Lesson 1-2.

1

Name _____

PROBLEM-SOLVING STRATEGY   R 1-3
Write a Number Sentence

Read and Understand

6 cats are on the steps.
3 more cats join them.
How many cats are there in all?

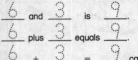
Add to join groups.
The addition sentence
6 + 3 = 9 can be used
to solve the problem.

Plan and Solve

You need to find out how many cats there are in all.

__6__ and __3__ is __9__.
__6__ plus __3__ equals __9__.
__6__ + __3__ = __9__ cats.

Look Back and Check

Did you answer the question?

Write a number sentence to solve each problem.

1. 5 puppies are playing.
3 puppies join them.
How many puppies are
there altogether?

__5__ plus __3__ equals __8__.
__5__ + __3__ = __8__

There are __8__ puppies altogether.

© Pearson Education, Inc. 2

Name _____

PROBLEM-SOLVING STRATEGY   P 1-3
Write a Number Sentence

Write a number sentence to solve the problem.

1. 6 goldfish are in one bowl.
4 goldfish are in another bowl.
How many goldfish are there altogether?

__6__ ⊕ __4__ ⊜ __10__ goldfish

2. There are 3 mice in a cage.
There are 4 mice in another cage.
How many mice are there in all?

__3__ ⊕ __4__ ⊜ __7__ mice

3. There are 2 frogs on a rock.
There are 6 frogs in the water.
How many frogs are there in all?

__2__ ⊕ __6__ ⊜ __8__ frogs

4. 3 kittens are playing.
8 kittens are sleeping.
How many kittens are there in all?

__3__ ⊕ __8__ ⊜ __11__ kittens

5. 5 butterflies are on a flower.
4 butterflies are on another flower.
How many butterflies are there in all?

__5__ ⊕ __4__ ⊜ __9__ butterflies

© Pearson Education, Inc. 2

Name _____

Taking Away to Subtract   R 1-4

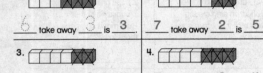
__11__ take away __6__ is __5__

Count the cubes.
Write the numbers.

1. __6__ take away __3__ is __3__

2. __7__ take away __2__ is __5__

3. __6__ take away __2__ is __4__

4. __7__ take away __3__ is __4__

5. __9__ take away __3__ is __6__

6. __8__ take away __5__ is __3__

7. __10__ take away __4__ is __6__

8. __6__ take away __4__ is __2__

© Pearson Education, Inc. 2

Name _____

Taking Away to Subtract   P 1-4

Write the numbers.

1. 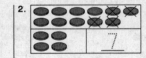 __6__

2. __7__

__9__ take away __3__ is __6__.   __11__ take away __4__ is __7__

3. 7 take away 1 is __6__   4. 5 take away 0 is __5__

5. 6 take away 2 is __4__   6. 8 take away 7 is __1__

7. 9 take away 4 is __5__   8. 7 take away 4 is __3__

9. 10 take away 3 is __7__   10. 8 take away 0 is __8__

Problem Solving *Algebra*

Circle the pennies that answer the question.

7. Beth started with
5 pennies.
She lost 2 pennies.
How many pennies
does Beth now have?

© **Pearson Education, Inc. 2**

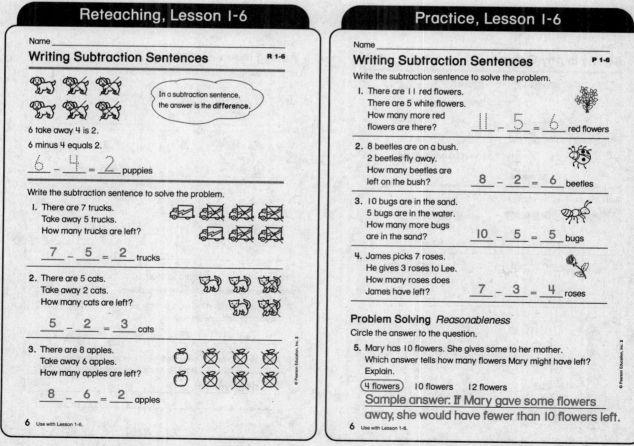

Reteaching, Lesson 1-5

Name _____

Comparing to Find How Many More   R 1-5

⊙ ⊙ ⊙ ⊙ ⊙
↓ ↓ ↓
□ □ □

To compare the number of circles and squares, match each circle with a square. There are 2 circles left over.

There are __5__ circles.

There are __3__ squares.

There are __2__ more circles than squares.

Compare the number of circles and squares.
Write the numbers.

1. ⊙⊙⊙⊙⊙⊙
   ↓ ↓
   □ □

   __6__ circles   __2__ squares

   __4__ more circles than squares.

2. ⊙ ⊙ ⊙ ⊙ ⊙
   ↓
   □

   __5__ circles   __1__ square

   __4__ more circles than squares.

3. ⊙⊙⊙⊙⊙
   ↓↓↓↓↓
   □□□□□

   __6__ circles   __5__ squares

   __1__ more circle than squares.

4. ⊙ ⊙ ⊙ ⊙
   ↓ ↓ ↓ ↓
   □ □ □ □

   __4__ circles   __4__ squares

   __0__ more circles than squares.

© Pearson Education, Inc. 2

Use with Lesson 1-5.   **5**

Practice, Lesson 1-5

Name _____

Comparing to Find How Many More   P 1-5

Compare the number of objects in each group.
Write the numbers.

1. How many more white ducks are there?

   __8__ white ducks   __3__ gray ducks   __5__ more white ducks

2. How many more spotted bears are there?

   __5__ spotted bears   __3__ white bears   __2__ more spotted bears

Reasoning *Writing in Math*   Stories may vary.

3. Write a math story to go with the picture.

   Sample answer: 3 flowers are in the striped pot. 2 flowers are in the spotted pot.

   How many more flowers are in the striped pot?

   __3__ flowers − __2__ flowers = __1__ more flower in the striped pot

© Pearson Education, Inc. 2

Use with Lesson 1-5.   **5**

Reteaching, Lesson 1-6

Name _____

Writing Subtraction Sentences   R 1-6

In a subtraction sentence, the answer is the difference.

6 take away 4 is 2.

6 minus 4 equals 2.

__6__ − __4__ = __2__ puppies

Write the subtraction sentence to solve the problem.

1. There are 7 trucks.
   Take away 5 trucks.
   How many trucks are left?

   __7__ − __5__ = __2__ trucks

2. There are 5 cats.
   Take away 2 cats.
   How many cats are left?

   __5__ − __2__ = __3__ cats

3. There are 8 apples.
   Take away 6 apples.
   How many apples are left?

   __8__ − __6__ = __2__ apples

© Pearson Education, Inc. 2

6 Use with Lesson 1-6.

Practice, Lesson 1-6

Name _____

Writing Subtraction Sentences   P 1-6

Write the subtraction sentence to solve the problem.

1. There are 11 red flowers.
   There are 5 white flowers.
   How many more red flowers are there?

   __11__ − __5__ = __6__ red flowers

2. 8 beetles are on a bush.
   2 beetles fly away.
   How many beetles are left on the bush?

   __8__ − __2__ = __6__ beetles

3. 10 bugs are in the sand.
   5 bugs are in the water.
   How many more bugs are in the sand?

   __10__ − __5__ = __5__ bugs

4. James picks 7 roses.
   He gives 3 roses to Lee.
   How many roses does James have left?

   __7__ − __3__ = __4__ roses

Problem Solving *Reasonableness*

Circle the answer to the question.

5. Mary has 10 flowers. She gives some to her mother. Which answer tells how many flowers Mary might have left? Explain.

   (4 flowers)   10 flowers   12 flowers

   Sample answer: If Mary gave some flowers away, she would have fewer than 10 flowers left.

© Pearson Education, Inc. 2

6 Use with Lesson 1-6.

3

Name _____

Choose an Operation

Which number sentence can be used to
solve the problem?

5 birds are in a tree.
3 birds join them.
How many birds are there in all?

7 frogs are on a log.
2 frogs hop away.
How many frogs are left?

(5 + 3 = 8)   8 − 3 = 5 | 5 + 2 = 7   (7 − 2 = 5)

Circle the number sentence that solves the problem.

1. 5 parrots are in a cage.
   4 parrots fly away.
   How many parrots are left?

   1 + 4 = 5   (5 − 4 = 1)

2. 6 kittens are in a box.
   1 kitten jumps in.
   How many kittens are
   there in all?

   (6 + 1 = 7)   7 − 1 = 6

Name _____

Choose an Operation

Circle **add** or **subtract**.
Then write the number sentence to solve the problem.

1. Sasha has 12 toy cars. She
   gives 6 of them to Michael.
   How many toy cars does
   Sasha have left?   add   (subtract)

   12 ⊖ 6 ⊜ 6   toy cars

2. Sara has 7 crayons.
   Bobby gives her 1 more
   crayon. How many crayons
   does Sara have in all?   (add)   subtract

   7 ⊕ 1 ⊜ 8   crayons

3. 8 children play a game.
   4 children go home.
   How many children are
   left playing the game?   add   (subtract)

   8 ⊖ 4 ⊜ 4   children

4. 5 children play hopscotch.
   3 children play jump rope.
   How many more children
   play hopscotch?   add   (subtract)

   5 ⊖ 3 ⊜ 2   children

Reasoning *Writing in Math*   Stories may vary.

5. Write a math story. Then write a number sentence to solve it.

   Sample answer: 9 books were on
   the table. Lisa took 4 books with her.
   How many books were left on the table?
   9 − 4 = 5 books

Name _____

Adding in Any Order

5 + 2 = 7   2 + 5 = 7

| Same addends in a different order. |

5 + 2 = 7   2 + 5 = 7 are **related addition facts.**

| same sum |

Write the numbers for each picture.

1.

   3 + 4 = 7   4 + 3 = 7

2.

   6 + 1 = 7   1 + 6 = 7

3.

   2
   + 4
   ____
   6

   4
   + 2
   ____
   6

Name _____

Adding in Any Order

Write the sum. Then write the related addition fact.

1. 2 + 4 = 6
   4 + 2 = 6

2. 7 + 1 = 8
   1 + 7 = 8

3. 9 + 2 = 11
   2 + 9 = 11

4. 5 + 3 = 8
   3 + 5 = 8

5.   6   4
     + 4   + 6
     10   10

6.   3   4
     + 4   + 3
     7   7

Problem Solving *Writing in Math*

Write a number sentence to solve the problem.

7. There are 4 birds in the nest. 3 birds join them.
   How many birds are there in all?

   4 ⊕ 3 ⊜ 7 birds

8. Change the order of the addends in the number sentence
   in Exercise 7. Write a story for this new number sentence.

   Stories will vary.

Name _____

Ways to Make 10

R 1-9

How many ways can you make 10?
Color the remaining cubes red.
Write the number sentence.

There is __1__ gray cube.

There are __9__ red cubes.

$1 + 9 = 10$

Find ways to make ten. Color the remaining cubes red.

1. $2 + 8 = 10$

2. $3 + 7 = 10$

3. $4 + 6 = 10$

Use two different colors. Color to show a way to make ten. Write the number sentence.

Number sentences may vary.

4. ___ + ___ = ___

5. Look at the pattern.
   Find the missing numbers.

10	+	0	=	5	+	5
9	+	1	=	4	+	6
8	+	2	=	3	+	7
7	+	3	=	2	+	8
6	+	4	=	1	+	9

© Pearson Education, Inc. 2

Name _____

Ways to Make 10

P 1-9

Find different ways to make 10.
Complete each number sentence.

1. $5 + 5 = 10$

2. $8 + 2 = 10$

3. $9 + 1 = 10$

4. $10 = 3 + 7$

5. $4 + 6 = 10$

6. $10 = 10 + 0$

Write five more ways to make 10. Use different number sentences from those in Exercises 1–3.

7. $1 + 9 = 10$

8. $2 + 8 = 10$

9. $0 + 10 = 10$

10. $7 + 3 = 10$

11. $6 + 4 = 10$

Order of number sentences may vary.

Problem Solving *Mental Math*

Use mental math to find the missing numbers.
Look for the pattern in each chart.

12. Make 8

0	1	2	3	4
8	7	6	5	4

13. Make 6

0	1	2	3
6	5	4	3

© Pearson Education, Inc. 2

Name _____

Fact Families

R 1-10

Fact families have the same three numbers.

Addition Facts

$3 + 5 = 8$

$5 + 3 = 8$

Subtraction Facts

$8 - 5 = 3$

$8 - 3 = 5$

These four related facts make up a **fact family**.

Complete each fact family.

1.

$5 + 6 = 11$

$6 + 5 = 11$

$11 - 6 = 5$

$11 - 5 = 6$

2.

| 3 |
| + 9 |
| 12 |

| 9 |
| + 3 |
| 12 |

| 12 |
| - 9 |
| 3 |

| 12 |
| - 3 |
| 9 |

© Pearson Education, Inc. 2

Name _____

Fact Families

P 1-10

Complete each fact family.

1. $8 + 2 = 10$
   $2 + 8 = 10$
   $10 - 2 = 8$
   $10 - 8 = 2$

2. $3 + 4 = 7$
   $4 + 3 = 7$
   $7 - 4 = 3$
   $7 - 3 = 4$

Write your own fact families. **Answers may vary.**

3. ___ + ___ = ___
   ___ + ___ = ___
   ___ - ___ = ___
   ___ - ___ = ___

4.

| 3 |
| 3 |
| + |
| 6 |

| 6 |
| - 3 |
| 3 |

Problem Solving *Number Sense*

Circle all the answers that go with the problem.

5. There are 5 boys at the party.
   There are 6 girls at the party.
   How many children are at the party?

   (5 + 6)   6 − 5   (11 children)

6. 5 boys left the party.
   Now how many children are at the party?

   11 + 5   (11 − 5)   (6 children)

© Pearson Education, Inc. 2

© Pearson Education, Inc. 2

5

Name _____

Finding the Missing Part   R 1-11

There are 9 cubes in all. $6 + \underline{3} = 9$

6 cubes are outside the cup.

How many cubes are

under the cup? $\underline{3}$ cubes are under the cup.

Use cubes. Find out how many objects are under the cup.

I.

There are 8 cubes in all. $4 + \underline{4} = 8$

4 cubes are outside the cup.

How many cubes are

under the cup? $\underline{4}$ cubes are under the cup.

2.

There are 11 cubes in all. $5 + \underline{6} = 11$

5 cubes are outside the cup.

How many cubes are

under the cup? $\underline{6}$ cubes are under the cup.

© Pearson Education, Inc. 2

Use with Lesson 1-11. II

Name _____

Finding the Missing Part   P 1-11

Use counters.

Find out how many objects are in the bag.

I. There are 8 balls in all.

How many balls are in the bag? $4 + \underline{4} = 8$

$\underline{4}$ balls are in the bag.

2. There are 9 yo-yos in all.

How many yo-yos are in the bag? $2 + \underline{7} = 9$

$\underline{7}$ yo-yos are in the bag.

3. There are 10 whistles in all.

How many whistles are in the bag? $6 + \underline{4} = 10$

$\underline{4}$ whistles are in the bag.

Problem Solving *Algebra*

4. Pick 3 numbers from the hat.

Write an addition and a

subtraction sentence.

Possible answer: $7 + 5 = 12$; $12 - 5 = 7$

© Pearson Education, Inc. 2

Use with Lesson 1-11. II

Name _____

PROBLEM-SOLVING APPLICATIONS   R 1-12

Frogs and Toads

Circle the number sentence that solves the problem.

5 frogs are on a rock.	9 frogs are on a rock.
3 frogs join them.	4 frogs jump off.
How many frogs in all?	How many frogs are left?
Add to join groups.	**Subtract to separate groups or to compare.**

$(5 + 3 = 8)$ $5 - 3 = 2$ $9 + 4 = 13$ $(9 - 4 = 5)$

$\underline{8}$ frogs in all. $\underline{5}$ frogs are left.

Circle the number sentence that solves the problem.

I. 10 toads are in a pond.

5 toads jump out.

How many toads are left?

$10 + 5 = 15$ $(10 - 5 = 5)$

$\underline{5}$ toads are left.

2. 8 bugs are on a leaf.

5 bugs join them.

How many bugs in all?

$8 - 5 = 3$ $(8 + 5 = 13)$

$\underline{13}$ bugs in all.

3. 6 lizards are on a log.

2 more lizards join them.

How many lizards in all?

$6 - 2 = 4$ $(6 + 2 = 8)$

$\underline{8}$ lizards in all.

4. 7 birds are in a tree.

1 bird flies away.

How many birds are left?

$(7 - 1 = 6)$ $7 + 1 = 8$

$\underline{6}$ birds are left.

© Pearson Education, Inc. 2

12 Use with Lesson 1-12.

Name _____

PROBLEM-SOLVING APPLICATIONS   P 1-12

Frogs and Toads

Solve the problems.

I. A frog eats 3 mealworms. A toad eats 7 mealworms.

How many more mealworms does the toad eat?

$7 - 3 = \underline{4}$ mealworms

2. There are 7 bullfrogs on a rock. 6 more bullfrogs join them.

How many bullfrogs in all are on the rock now?

$\underline{7} \oplus \underline{6} \ominus \underline{13}$ bullfrogs

3. One American toad is 2 inches long. A second American toad is 4 inches long. How long are the two toads together?

$\underline{2} \oplus \underline{4} \ominus \underline{6}$ inches

Writing in Math

4. Write a number story about a frog who jumps and then jumps again.

Sample answer:

The frog jumped 2 feet. The frog jumped 3 more feet. How far did the frog jump?

$2 + 3 = 5$ feet

5. Stan has 11 tree frogs. Joy has 4 tree frogs.

How many more tree frogs does Stan have?

$\underline{11} \ominus \underline{4} \ominus \underline{7}$ tree frogs

© Pearson Education, Inc. 2

12 Use with Lesson 1-12.

© **Pearson** Education, Inc. **2**

Name _____   R 2-1

Counting On

You can use the number line to count on.

To add, **count on** 1, 2, or 3 from the larger number.

12 + 3 = 15   Start at 12.   Count on 13, 14, 15.

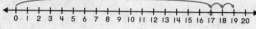
0 1 2 3 4 5 6 7 8 9 10 11 12 13 14 15 16 17 18 19 20

Use the number lines.
Count on to find each sum.

0 1 2 3 4 5 6 7 8 9 10 11 12 13 14 15 16 17 18 19 20

1. 17 + 2 = 19

0 1 2 3 4 5 6 7 8 9 10 11 12 13 14 15 16 17 18 19 20

2. 14 + 3 = 17

0 1 2 3 4 5 6 7 8 9 10 11 12 13 14 15 16 17 18 19 20

3. 15 + 3 = 18

Count on to find each sum.

4. 14 + 2 = 16   18 + 2 = 20   13 + 3 = 16

5. 16 + 3 = 19   13 + 1 = 14   19 + 1 = 20

© Pearson Education, Inc. 2

Use with Lesson 2-1. **13**

Name _____   P 2-1

Counting On

Count on to find each sum.

1. 11 + 3 = 14   14 + 2 = 16   18 + 3 = 21

2. 2 + 17 = 19   17 = 16 + 1   16 = 2 + 14

3. 19 + 2 = 21   13 = 11 + 2   3 + 19 = 22

4. 15 = 13 + 2   18 + 1 = 19   2 + 15 = 17

5. 13 + 3 = 16   2 + 12 = 14   14 = 3 + 11

6.
15	13	12	18	12	19
+3	+2	+2	+3	+1	+3
18	15	14	21	13	22

7.
14	17	13	19	16	12
+3	+1	+2	+2	+2	+3
17	18	15	21	18	15

Problem Solving *Number Sense*

Write a number sentence to solve each story. Solve.

8. Pam bought 13 flowers. Mark bought 3 flowers. How many flowers did they buy in all?

13 + 3 = 16 flowers

9. Lee collected 16 rocks. Meg collected 2 rocks. How many rocks did they collect in all?

16 + 2 = 18 rocks

© Pearson Education, Inc. 2

Use with Lesson 2-1. **13**

Name _____   R 2-2

Doubles Facts to 18

Find 3 + 3.

Draw 3 more dots to show the double.
Then write the addition sentence.

3 + 3 = 6 is a **doubles fact**. Both addends are the same.

3 + 3 = 6

Draw dots on the domino to show the double.
Then write the addition sentence.

1.
4 + 4 = 8

2.
5 + 5 = 10

3.
6 + 6 = 12

4.
7 + 7 = 14

5.
8 + 8 = 16

6.
9 + 9 = 18

© Pearson Education, Inc. 2

14 Use with Lesson 2-2.

Name _____   P 2-2

Doubles Facts to 18

Solve. Circle the doubles facts.

1. (12 = 6 + 6)   16 + 2 = 18   17 = 3 + 14

2. 15 + 1 = 16   (2 = 1 + 1)   2 + 18 = 20

3. (7 + 7 = 14)   16 = 13 + 3   (8 + 8 = 16)

4.
15	9	11	19	2	16
+3	+9	+2	+1	+2	+3
18	18	13	20	4	19

5.
6	16	1	14	5	18
+6	+1	+1	+2	+5	+3
12	17	2	16	10	21

6.
3	17	15	8	13	0
+3	+1	+2	+8	+2	+0
6	18	17	16	15	0

Problem Solving *Visual Thinking*

Draw a picture to solve the problem.
Write the number sentence.

7. Carissa counted 5 black buttons. Maurice counted the same number of white buttons. How many buttons did they count in all?

5 + 5 = 10

Drawings should show 2 groups of 5 objects each.

© Pearson Education, Inc. 2

14 Use with Lesson 2-2.

Name _____

Doubles Plus 1

R 2-3

You can use a doubles fact to find a doubles-plus-1 fact.

$6 + 7 = 13$ is a doubles-plus-1 fact because it is equal to $6 + 6 = 12$ plus one more.

$6 + 6 = \underline{12}$

Doubles Fact

$6 + 7 = \underline{13}$

Doubles-Plus-1 Fact

Add. Use doubles facts to help you.

1.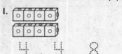

$\underline{4} + \underline{4} = \underline{8}$ $\underline{4} + \underline{5} = \underline{9}$

2.

$\underline{5} + \underline{5} = \underline{10}$ $\underline{5} + \underline{6} = \underline{11}$

3.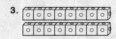

$\underline{8} + \underline{8} = \underline{16}$ $\underline{8} + \underline{9} = \underline{17}$

Use with Lesson 2-3. 15

Name _____

Doubles Plus 1

P 2-3

Add. Use doubles facts to help you.

1.	5 + 5 10	8 + 9 17	9 + 9 18	5 + 6 11	2 + 2 4	4 + 3 7
2.	10 + 9 19	7 + 7 14	8 + 7 15	0 + 0 0	4 + 5 9	8 + 8 16
3.	7 + 8 15	6 + 7 13	4 + 4 8	6 + 5 11	3 + 3 6	2 + 3 5

4. $7 + 6 = \underline{13}$ $5 + 4 = \underline{9}$ $\underline{7} = 3 + 4$

5. $9 + 10 = \underline{19}$ $4 + 4 = \underline{8}$ $9 + 8 = \underline{17}$

Problem Solving *Writing in Math*

6. Use pictures, numbers, or words to tell how $6 + 8$ and $6 + 6$ are related.

Answers may vary. Have children explain that since 8 is 2 more than 6, the sum of $6 + 8$, or 14, is 2 more than $6 + 6$, or 12.

Use with Lesson 2-3. 15

Name _____

Using Strategies to Add Three Numbers

R 2-4

You can use different strategies to add 3 numbers.

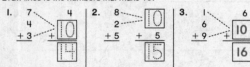

Make ten to add.
Draw lines to the numbers that make 10.

1. 7
4
+ 3   [10]
+ [10]
14

2. 8
2
+ 5   [10]
+ 5
15

3. 1
6
+ 9   6
+ [10]
16

Use a doubles fact or count on to add.
Draw lines from the numbers added first.

4. 7
7
+ 5   [14]
+ 5
19

5. 8
4
+ 8   4
+ [16]
20

6. 2
6
+ 7   2
+ [13]
15

7. 4
2
+ 7   [6]
+ 7
13

8. 1
7
+ 7   8
+ [8]
16

9. 6
5
+ 3   [11]
+ 3
14

16 Use with Lesson 2-4.

Name _____

Using Strategies to Add Three Numbers

P 2-4

Add. Try different ways.

1. $3 + 7 + 3 = \underline{13}$ 2. $\underline{15} = 3 + 6 + 6$

3. $6 + 4 + 5 = \underline{15}$ 4. $\underline{16} = 8 + 0 + 8$

5.	10 3 + 5 18	9 2 + 2 13	6 5 + 4 15	4 1 + 9 14	4 6 + 5 15	8 3 + 8 19
6.	5 8 + 4 17	6 3 + 7 16	8 3 + 6 17	2 8 + 8 18	5 7 + 3 15	9 0 + 8 17

Problem Solving *Algebra*

Find the missing numbers. The same shapes are the same numbers.

The numbers in ◯ are sums. Add across and down.

7.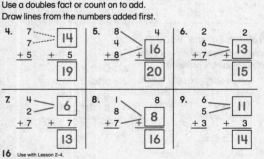

8.

△ = $\underline{2}$ ▢ = $\underline{3}$ ▱ = $\underline{4}$ ⬠ = $\underline{5}$

16 Use with Lesson 2-4.

© Pearson Education, Inc. 2

8

Name _____

Making 10 to Add 9

R 2-5

Find 9 + 6.

9 + 6 equals $\underline{5}$

$10 + \underline{5}$

$\underline{9} + \underline{6}$ $\underline{10} + \underline{5}$ 9 + 6 = $\underline{15}$

Use counters and Workmat 2. Make 10 to find each sum.

1. Find 9 + 7.

9 + 7 equals

$10 + \underline{6}$

$\underline{9} + \underline{7}$ $\underline{10} + \underline{6}$ 9 + 7 = $\underline{16}$

2. Find 9 + 5.

9 + 5 equals

$10 + \underline{4}$

$\underline{9} + \underline{5}$ $\underline{10} + \underline{4}$ 9 + 5 = $\underline{14}$

© Pearson Education, Inc. 2

Use with Lesson 2-5. **17**

Name _____

Making 10 to Add 9

P 2-5

Add. Use counters and Workmat 3 if you need to.

1.	9 +3 = $\underline{12}$	6 +9 = 15	0 +9 = 9	9 +8 = 17	2 +9 = 11	5 +9 = 14

2.	9 +7 = 16	9 +1 = 10	3 +9 = 12	9 +8 = 17	5 +9 = 14	9 +6 = 15

3.	9 +5 = 14	4 +9 = 13	7 +9 = 16	9 +5 = 14	9 +2 = 11	8 +9 = 17

4. 9 + 7 = $\underline{16}$ 6 + 9 = $\underline{15}$ 4 + 9 = $\underline{13}$

Problem Solving *Reasoning*

Solve by using pictures, numbers, or words.

5. Shana had 9 pins in her collection. She bought more pins. Now she has 17 pins. How many pins did Shana buy?

Answers will vary. Pictures should show 9 and 8 pins. Number sentences should show 8 + 9 = 17, 9 + 8 = 17, or 17 − 9 = 8. Words should reveal the missing addend of 8 or 8 + 9 = 17

© Pearson Education, Inc. 2

Use with Lesson 2-5. **17**

Name _____

Making 10 to Add 7 or 8

R 2-6

Find 8 + 5.

8 + 5 equals

$10 + \underline{3}$

$\underline{8} + \underline{5}$ $\underline{10} + \underline{3}$ 8 + 5 = $\underline{13}$

Make 10 to find each sum. Use counters and Workmat 2.

1. Find 7 + 6.

7 + 6 equals

$10 + \underline{3}$

$\underline{7} + \underline{6}$ $\underline{10} + \underline{3}$ 7 + 6 = $\underline{13}$

2. Find 8 + 3.

8 + 3 equals

$10 + \underline{1}$

$\underline{8} + \underline{3}$ $\underline{10} + \underline{1}$ 8 + 3 = $\underline{11}$

© Pearson Education, Inc. 2

18 Use with Lesson 2-6.

Name _____

Making 10 to Add 7 or 8

P 2-6

Add. Use counters and Workmat 3 if you need to.

1.	8 +3 = 11	5 +9 = 14	4 +7 = 11	8 +8 = 16	7 +9 = 16	9 +5 = 14

2.	8 +7 = 15	4 +8 = 12	6 +7 = 13	8 +6 = 14	5 +7 = 12	7 +8 = 15

3. 4 + 8 = $\underline{12}$ 10 + 7 = $\underline{17}$ 0 + 8 = $\underline{8}$

4. 7 + 7 = $\underline{14}$ 9 + 3 = $\underline{12}$ $\underline{19}$ = 9 + 10

Problem Solving *Algebra*

Find the pattern. Write the missing numbers.

5.
7 + 9	=	10 + 6
7 + 8	=	10 + 5
7 + 7	=	10 + 4
7 + 6	=	10 + 3
7 + 5	=	10 + 2

© Pearson Education, Inc. 2

18 Use with Lesson 2-6.

© Pearson Education, Inc. 2

9

Name _____

Write a Number Sentence

Read and Understand

Tim and Rosa played 3 games
of tossing a bean bag.
Here are their scores.

Players	Game 1	Game 2	Game 3
Tim	4	6	3
Rosa	7	2	5

How many points did Tim and
Rosa score altogether in Game 1?

Plan and Solve

You need to find out how many points
Tim and Rosa scored in Game 1.

Tim's score ___4___   Rosa's score ___7___

Write a number sentence to solve.

___4___ + ___7___ = ___11___ points

Look Back and Check

Check your work. Does your answer make sense?

Write a number sentence to solve the problem.
Use the table to help you.

1. How many points did Tim
   and Rosa score altogether
   in Game 2?

   ___6 + 2___ = ___8___ points

2. How many points did
   Rosa score altogether in
   Games 2 and 3?

   ___2 + 5___ = ___7___ points

Use with Lesson 2-7.   19

Name _____

Write a Number Sentence

Write a number sentence to solve the problem.
Use the table to help you.

Game Scores			
Teams	Game 1	Game 2	Game 3
Robins	7	4	6
Bluejays	5	8	5

1. How many points did the Bluejays score
   altogether in Games 1 and 2?

   ___5 + 8___ = ___13___ points

2. How many points did the Robins score altogether
   in Games 1 and 2?

   ___7 + 4___ = ___11___ points

3. Which team had scored
   more points after Game 2?   ___Bluejays___

4. How many points did the Robins score altogether?

   ___7 + 4 + 6___ = ___17___ points

5. How many points did the Bluejays score altogether?

   ___5 + 8 + 5___ = ___18___ points

6. Which team, the Robins or the Bluejays,
   scored more points altogether?   ___Bluejays___

Use with Lesson 2-7.   19

Name _____

Counting Back

You can count back to subtract.

$16 - 2 =$ ___14___

1	2	3	4	5	6	7	8	9	10
11	12	13	14	15	16	17	18	19	20

Find 16 on the hundreds chart.
Then count back, first to 15, then to 14.

Subtract. Use the hundreds chart to count back.

1. $14 - 2 =$ ___12___

1	2	3	4	5	6	7	8	9	10
11	12	13	14	15	16	17	18	19	20

2. $10 - 1 =$ ___9___

1	2	3	4	5	6	7	8	9	10
11	12	13	14	15	16	17	18	19	20

Subtract. Use the hundreds chart to help you.

1	2	3	4	5	6	7	8	9	10
11	12	13	14	15	16	17	18	19	20

3. $16 - 1 =$ ___15___ $13 - 1 =$ ___12___ $14 - 1 =$ ___13___

4. $10 - 2 =$ ___8___ $17 - 2 =$ ___15___ $19 - 2 =$ ___17___

5. $18 - 2 =$ ___16___ $15 - 2 =$ ___13___ $11 - 2 =$ ___9___

Name _____

Counting Back

Subtract. Use the number line if you need to.

0 1 2 3 4 5 6 7 8 9 10 11 12 13 14 15 16 17 18 19 20

1. $16 - 2 =$ ___14___ $14 - 3 =$ ___11___   ___12___ $= 13 - 1$

2. $15 - 2 =$ ___13___   ___9___ $= 12 - 3$ $18 - 2 =$ ___16___

3.
$$11 - 3 = 8$$
$$14 - 2 = 12$$
$$19 - 1 = 18$$
$$17 - 3 = 14$$
$$13 - 2 = 11$$
$$12 - 2 = 10$$

4.
$$11 - 2 = 9$$
$$17 - 2 = 15$$
$$13 - 3 = 10$$
$$15 - 3 = 12$$
$$18 - 1 = 17$$
$$16 - 3 = 13$$

5.
$$19 - 3 = 16$$
$$14 - 1 = 13$$
$$15 - 2 = 13$$
$$18 - 3 = 15$$
$$13 - 2 = 11$$
$$19 - 1 = 18$$

Problem Solving *Writing in Math*

Write a story or draw a picture
to go with the problem.
Then solve.

6. $16 - 5 =$ ___11___

Children's stories
or drawings should
show that 11 is the
difference between
16 and 5.

© Pearson Education, Inc. 2

10

Reteaching, Lesson 2-9

Name _____

Thinking Doubles to Subtract

R 2-9

$6 - 3 = ?$

Think of a doubles fact.

$3 + \underline{3} = 6$ So, $6 - 3 = \underline{3}$.

Use doubles facts to help you subtract.
Cross out the dots you take away.

1. $8 - 4 = ?$

$4 + \underline{4} = 8$ $8 - 4 = \underline{4}$

2. $10 - 5 = ?$

$5 + \underline{5} = 10$ $10 - 5 = \underline{5}$

3. $12 - 6 = ?$

$6 + \underline{6} = 12$ $12 - 6 = \underline{6}$

4. $14 - 7 = ?$

$7 + \underline{7} = 14$ $14 - 7 = \underline{7}$

5. $16 - 8 = ?$

$8 + \underline{8} = 16$ $16 - 8 = \underline{8}$

6. $18 - 9 = ?$

$9 + \underline{9} = 18$ $18 - 9 = \underline{9}$

Practice, Lesson 2-9

Name _____

Thinking Doubles to Subtract

P 2-9

Subtract. Write the doubles fact that helps you.

1. $10 - 5 = \underline{5}$

$\underline{5} + \underline{5} = 10$

If $5 + 5 = 10$
then $10 - 5 = 5$

2. $20 - 10 = \underline{10}$

$\underline{10} + \underline{10} = 20$

3. $\underline{6} = 12 - 6$

$\underline{12} = \underline{6} + \underline{6}$

4. $6 - 3 = \underline{3}$

$\underline{3} + \underline{3} = 6$

5. $\underline{7} = 14 - 7$

$\underline{14} = \underline{7} + \underline{7}$

6. $\begin{array}{r} 8 \\ -\ 4 \\ \hline \end{array}$ $\boxed{4}$ $+ \boxed{4} \atop \boxed{8}$

7. $\begin{array}{r} 18 \\ -\ 9 \\ \hline \end{array}$ $\boxed{9}$ $+ \boxed{9} \atop \boxed{18}$

Problem Solving *Writing in Math*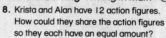

8. Krista and Alan have 12 action figures. How could they share the action figures so they each have an equal amount?

   Each child would get 6 action figures.
   $6 + 6 = 12$

Reteaching, Lesson 2-10

Name _____

Thinking Addition to Subtract

R 2-10

Think addition to find the difference for $14 - 6$.

Addition Fact   **Subtraction Fact**

Think $6 + \underline{8} = 14$.   So, $14 - 6 = \underline{8}$.

Use addition facts to help you subtract.

1. Think $9 + \underline{4} = 13$.   So, $13 - 9 = \underline{4}$.

2. Think $7 + \underline{5} = 12$.   So, $12 - 7 = \underline{5}$.

3. Think $8 + \underline{9} = 17$.   So, $17 - 8 = \underline{9}$.

4. Think $9 + \underline{6} = 15$.   So, $15 - 9 = \underline{6}$.

Practice, Lesson 2-10

Name _____

Thinking Addition to Subtract

P 2-10

Solve. Draw a line to match each subtraction fact with its related addition fact.

1. $14 - 8 = \underline{6}$ $5 + \underline{6} = 11$

   $16 - 7 = \underline{9}$ $2 + \underline{16} = 18$

   $11 - 5 = \underline{6}$ $8 + \underline{6} = 14$

   $18 - 2 = \underline{16}$ $7 + \underline{9} = 16$

2. $\underline{9} = 15 - 6$ $13 = 5 + \underline{8}$

   $\underline{5} = 12 - 7$ $15 = 6 + \underline{9}$

   $\underline{14} = 17 - 3$ $17 = 3 + \underline{14}$

   $\underline{8} = 13 - 5$ $12 = 7 + \underline{5}$

Problem Solving *Mental Math*

3. Randy has 20¢. He bought a used toy truck for 14¢. Circle the used toy that he has enough money left to buy.

8¢

10¢

5¢

Name _____

PROBLEM-SOLVING SKILL   R 2-11

Use Data from a Picture

What does the cube weigh?

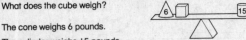

The cone weighs 6 pounds.
The cylinder weighs 15 pounds.

The cube weighs   If   6 + _9_ = 15,
_9_ pounds.   then   15 − 6 = _9_ .

Use the picture to find the missing number.
Write the number sentence.

1. What does the sphere weigh?

   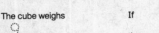

   The cube weighs 7 pounds.
   The cone weighs 12 pounds.

   The sphere weighs   If   _5_ + 7 = 12,
   _5_ pounds.   then   12 − _5_ = 7.

2. What does the cube weigh?

   The cylinder weighs 4 pounds.
   The sphere weighs 12 pounds.

   The cube weighs   If   4 + _8_ = 12,
   _8_ pounds.   then   12 − 4 = _8_ .

Name _____

PROBLEM-SOLVING SKILL   P 2-11

Use Data from a Picture

Find the missing number.
Write the number sentence.

1. What does the cube weigh?

   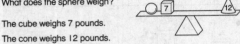

   If _8_ + 5 = 13,
   then 13 − 5 = _8_
   The cube weighs _8_ pounds.

2. What does the cylinder weigh?

   If 6 + _4_ = 10,
   then 10 − 6 = _4_
   The cylinder weighs _4_ pounds.

Reasoning
Write the missing number for each sentence.

3. _9_ + 8 = 17   4. 14 − _5_ = 9

   7 + _6_ = 13   15 − _7_ = 8

Name _____

PROBLEM-SOLVING APPLICATIONS   R 2-12

Baby Birds

1. 2 birds were at the birdbath and 3 more joined them. Then, 4 more birds came. How many birds were at the birdbath in all?

   _2 + 3 + 4 = 9_ birds

2. The mother and father bird make many hunting trips each hour. How many hunting trips did the mother make during the second hour?

	Mom	Dad	Total
Hour 1	8 trips	12 trips	20 trips
Hour 2	_9_ trips	10 trips	19 trips

   _9_ + 10 = 19 trips

   She made _9_ trips during the second hour.

3. The father bird caught 5 worms the first hour and 9 worms the second hour. How many more worms did he catch the second hour?

   _9_ ⊖ _5_ = _4_ more worms

4. The mother bird caught 3 worms the first hour and 5 worms the second hour. How many worms did she catch in all?

   _3_ ⊕ _5_ = _8_ worms in all

Name _____

PROBLEM-SOLVING APPLICATIONS   P 2-12

Baby Birds

Solve.

1. A nest has 13 eggs, and 5 of the eggs hatch. How many more eggs need to hatch?

   _13_ − _5_ = _8_ eggs

2. A group of nestlings is 8 days old. In 9 more days, they will be ready to leave the nest. How old will they be then?

   _8_ ⊕ _9_ = _17_ days old

3. Look at the chart. How many nestlings are in the second family?

	Parents	Nestlings	Total
Family 1	2	4	6
Family 2	2	_6_	8

   2 + _6_ = 8

   There are _6_ nestlings in the second family.

Writing in Math

4. A group of 3 birds was at the bird feeder. Then 12 more birds came and chased them away. How many birds were left at the bird feeder?

   There were 12 birds left at the bird feeder.

Name _____

Counting with Tens and Ones

R 3-1

A class made a snack.
The children put 10 raisins on each piece of celery.
Some raisins were left over.

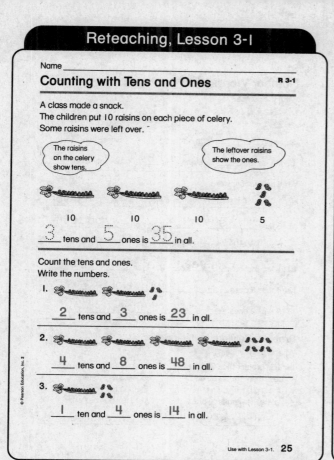

The raisins on the celery show tens.

The leftover raisins show the ones.

10   10   10   5

__3__ tens and __5__ ones is __35__ in all.

Count the tens and ones.
Write the numbers.

1. __2__ tens and __3__ ones is __23__ in all.

2. __4__ tens and __8__ ones is __48__ in all.

3. __1__ ten and __4__ ones is __14__ in all.

Use with Lesson 3-1. **25**

© Pearson Education, Inc. 2

Name _____

Counting with Tens and Ones

P 3-1

Circle groups of ten. Count the tens and ones.
Write the numbers.

1.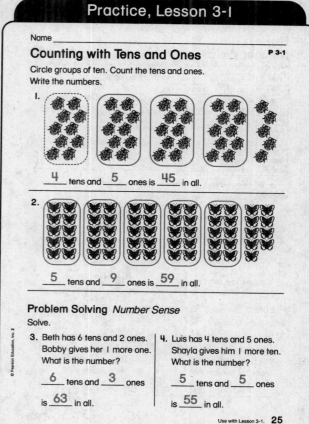

__4__ tens and __5__ ones is __45__ in all.

2. __5__ tens and __9__ ones is __59__ in all.

Problem Solving *Number Sense*
Solve.

3. Beth has 6 tens and 2 ones. Bobby gives her 1 more one. What is the number?

__6__ tens and __3__ ones is __63__ in all.

4. Luis has 4 tens and 5 ones. Shayla gives him 1 more ten. What is the number?

__5__ tens and __5__ ones is __55__ in all.

Use with Lesson 3-1. **25**

© Pearson Education, Inc. 2

Name _____

Using Tens and Ones

R 3-2

Count the cubes. Then count the tens and ones.
Write how many there are.

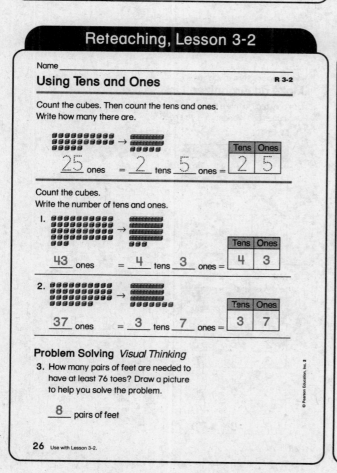

__25__ ones = __2__ tens __5__ ones

Tens	Ones
2	5

Count the cubes.
Write the number of tens and ones.

1. __43__ ones = __4__ tens __3__ ones

Tens	Ones
4	3

2. __37__ ones = __3__ tens __7__ ones

Tens	Ones
3	7

Problem Solving *Visual Thinking*

3. How many pairs of feet are needed to have at least 76 toes? Draw a picture to help you solve the problem.

__8__ pairs of feet

26 Use with Lesson 3-2.

© Pearson Education, Inc. 2

Name _____

Using Tens and Ones

P 3-2

Draw lines to match the numbers.
Use cubes and Workmat 4 if you need to.

1.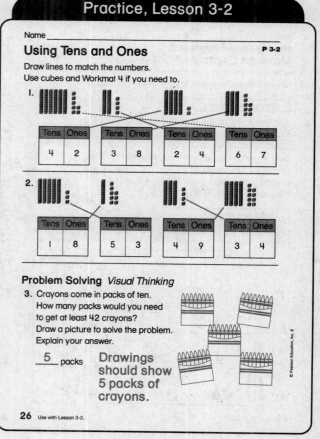

Tens	Ones
4	2

Tens	Ones
3	8

Tens	Ones
2	4

Tens	Ones
6	7

2.

Tens	Ones
1	8

Tens	Ones
5	3

Tens	Ones
4	9

Tens	Ones
3	4

Problem Solving *Visual Thinking*

3. Crayons come in packs of ten. How many packs would you need to get at least 42 crayons? Draw a picture to solve the problem. Explain your answer.

__5__ packs   Drawings should show 5 packs of crayons.

26 Use with Lesson 3-2.

© Pearson Education, Inc. 2

13

Number Words

Name _____ R 3-3

Ones	Teens	Tens
1 one	11 eleven	10 ten
2 two	12 twelve	20 twenty
3 three	13 thirteen	30 thirty
4 four	14 fourteen	40 forty
5 five	15 fifteen	50 fifty
6 six	16 sixteen	60 sixty
7 seven	17 seventeen	70 seventy
8 eight	18 eighteen	80 eighty
9 nine	19 nineteen	90 ninety

Write the number.

7 tens and 8 ones is 78.

78 has two **digits**.

Write the number word.

seventy and **eight** is seventy-eight

Write the number and the number word.

1. 2 tens and 9 ones is 29. twenty-nine
2. 6 tens and 3 ones is 63. sixty-three
3. 9 tens and 2 ones is 92. ninety-two
4. 8 tens and 6 ones is 86. eighty-six

Problem Solving *Number Sense*

What is the number?

5. It is greater than 43 and less than 52. If you add the digits, the sum is 8. Write the number word.

forty-four

6. It is less than 60 and greater than 55. If you add the digits, the sum is 13. Write the number.

58

Use with Lesson 3-3. **27**

Number Words

Name _____ P 3-3

Write the number.

1. eight 8   twenty-five 25   forty-nine 49
2. sixty 60   thirteen 13   ninety-two 92
3. fifty-seven 57   eighty-four 84   seventy-three 73

Write the number word.

4. 18 eighteen   5. 77 seventy-seven
6. 5 tens fifty   7. 14 ones fourteen
8. 27 twenty-seven   9. 50 fifty
10. 1 ten 8 ones eighteen   11. 3 tens thirty
12. 4 tens 8 ones forty-eight
13. 9 tens 2 ones ninety-two

Problem Solving *Number Sense*

What is the number?

14. It is greater than 30 and less than 40. If you add the digits, the sum is 10. Write the number word.

thirty-seven

15. It is greater than 7 tens and less than 8 tens. The number has 4 ones. Write the number word.

seventy-four

Use with Lesson 3-3. **27**

Name _____ R 3-4

PROBLEM-SOLVING STRATEGY

Make an Organized List

Make 40 as many ways as you can by using groups of ten.

Read and Understand

You need to find groups of 10 that make 40.

Plan and Solve

Use tens models to help you find groups that make 40. Look at the tens shown in the first group. Draw the tens needed in the second group to make 40. Write the missing numbers in the list.

Look Back and Check

Check to see if each row makes 40.

	Tens	Tens	Total
1.	0 tens	4 tens	40
2.	1 ten	3 tens	40
3.	2 tens	2 tens	40
4.	3 tens	1 ten	40

28 Use with Lesson 3-4.

Name _____ P 3-4

PROBLEM-SOLVING STRATEGY

Make an Organized List

Use only tens to make the number in two parts.
Use cubes and Workmat 1 if you need to.

1. Make 40.

Tens	Tens	Total
0	4	40
1	3	40
2	2	40
3	1	40
4	0	40

2. Make 80.

Tens	Tens	Total
0	8	80
1	7	80
2	6	80
3	5	80
4	4	80
5	3	80
6	2	80
7	1	80
8	0	80

3. Make 70.

Tens	Tens	Total
0	7	70
1	6	70
2	5	70
3	4	70
4	3	70
5	2	70
6	1	70
7	0	70

28 Use with Lesson 3-4.

© Pearson Education, Inc. 2

Comparing Numbers

R 3-5

Name _____

You can compare numbers using words or the signs >, <, or =.

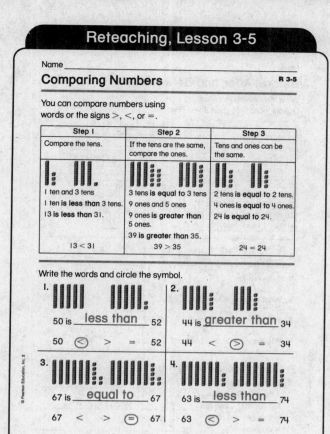

Step 1	Step 2	Step 3
Compare the tens.	If the tens are the same, compare the ones.	Tens and ones can be the same.
1 ten and 3 tens	3 tens is equal to 3 tens	2 tens is equal to 2 tens.
1 ten is less than 3 tens.	9 ones and 5 ones	4 ones is equal to 4 ones.
13 is less than 31.	9 ones is greater than 5 ones.	24 is equal to 24.
	39 is greater than 35.	
13 < 31	39 > 35	24 = 24

Write the words and circle the symbol.

1. 50 is __less than__ 52

50 (<) > = 52

2. 44 is __greater than__ 34

44 < (>) = 34

3. 67 is __equal to__ 67

67 < > (=) 67

4. 63 is __less than__ 74

63 (<) > = 74

Use with Lesson 3-5. 29

Comparing Numbers

P 3-5

Name _____

Write >, <, or =.

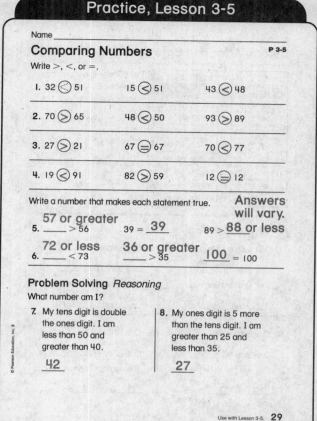

1. 32 (<) 51   15 (<) 51   43 (<) 48

2. 70 (>) 65   48 (<) 50   93 (>) 89

3. 27 (>) 21   67 (=) 67   70 (<) 77

4. 19 (<) 91   82 (>) 59   12 (=) 12

Write a number that makes each statement true.   **Answers will vary.**

5. ___ > 56 (57 or greater)   39 = __39__   89 > __88 or less__

6. ___ < 73 (72 or less)   ___ > 35 (36 or greater)   __100__ = 100

Problem Solving *Reasoning*

What number am I?

7. My tens digit is double the ones digit. I am less than 50 and greater than 40.

__42__

8. My ones digit is 5 more than the tens digit. I am greater than 25 and less than 35.

__27__

Use with Lesson 3-5. 29

Finding the Closest Ten

R 3-6

Name _____

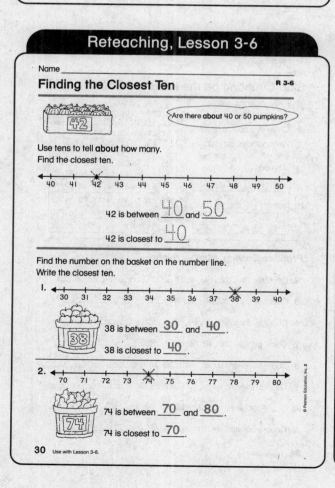

Are there **about** 40 or 50 pumpkins?

Use tens to tell **about** how many. Find the closest ten.

42 is between __40__ and __50__

42 is closest to __40__

Find the number on the basket on the number line. Write the closest ten.

1. 38 is between __30__ and __40__.

38 is closest to __40__.

2. 74 is between __70__ and __80__.

74 is closest to __70__.

30 Use with Lesson 3-6.

Finding the Closest Ten

P 3-6

Name _____

Find the number on the number line. Write the closest ten.

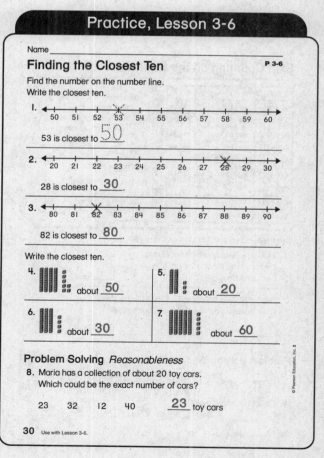

1. 53 is closest to __50__

2. 28 is closest to __30__

3. 82 is closest to __80__

Write the closest ten.

4. about __50__

5. about __20__

6. about __30__

7. about __60__

Problem Solving *Reasonableness*

8. Maria has a collection of about 20 toy cars. Which could be the exact number of cars?

23   32   12   40   __23__ toy cars

30 Use with Lesson 3-6.

15

Before, After, and Between

R 3-7

Name _____

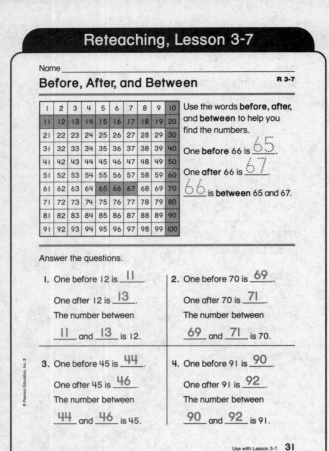

Use the words **before, after,** and **between** to help you find the numbers.

One **before** 66 is 65.

One **after** 66 is 67.

66 is **between** 65 and 67.

Answer the questions.

1. One before 12 is 11.
   One after 12 is 13.
   The number between
   11 and 13 is 12.

2. One before 70 is 69.
   One after 70 is 71.
   The number between
   69 and 71 is 70.

3. One before 45 is 44.
   One after 45 is 46.
   The number between
   44 and 46 is 45.

4. One before 91 is 90.
   One after 91 is 92.
   The number between
   90 and 92 is 91.

Use with Lesson 3-7. **31**

Before, After, and Between

P 3-7

Name _____

Write the missing numbers.
Use the hundreds chart if you need to.

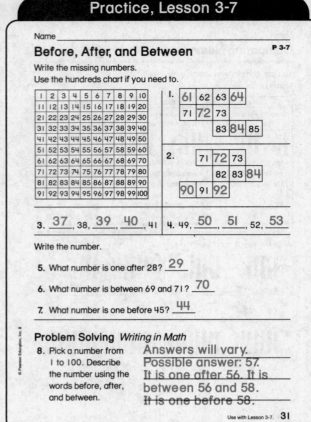

1. | 61 | 62 | 63 | 64 |
   | 71 | 72 | 73 | |
   | | | 83 | 84 | 85 |

2. | 71 | 72 | 73 |
   | | 82 | 83 | 84 |
   | 90 | 91 | 92 |

3. 37, 38, 39, 40, 41
4. 49, 50, 51, 52, 53

Write the number.

5. What number is one after 28? 29
6. What number is between 69 and 71? 70
7. What number is one before 45? 44

Problem Solving *Writing in Math*

8. Pick a number from 1 to 100. Describe the number using the words before, after, and between.

Answers will vary.
Possible answer: 57.
It is one after 56. It is
between 56 and 58.
~~It is one before 58.~~

Use with Lesson 3-7. **31**

Skip Counting on the Hundred Chart

R 3-8

Name _____

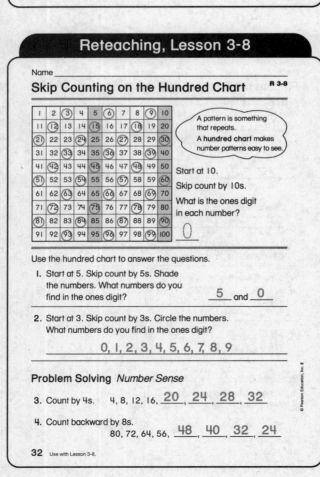

A pattern is something that repeats.

A **hundred chart** makes number patterns easy to see.

Start at 10.
Skip count by 10s.
What is the ones digit in each number? 0

Use the hundred chart to answer the questions.

1. Start at 5. Skip count by 5s. Shade the numbers. What numbers do you find in the ones digit? 5 and 0

2. Start at 3. Skip count by 3s. Circle the numbers. What numbers do you find in the ones digit?
   0, 1, 2, 3, 4, 5, 6, 7, 8, 9

Problem Solving *Number Sense*

3. Count by 4s. 4, 8, 12, 16, 20, 24, 28, 32

4. Count backward by 8s.
   80, 72, 64, 56, 48, 40, 32, 24

32 Use with Lesson 3-8.

Skip Counting on the Hundred Chart

P 3-8

Name _____

1. Finish coloring skip counts by 10s.
2. Circle skip counts by 3s.
3. What patterns do you see with skip counts by 10s and 3s?

Tens are up and down in a column.
Threes are diagonal.

Problem Solving *Number Sense*

4. Count by 2s. 12, 14, 16, 18, 20, 22, 24, 26
5. Count by 3s. 30, 33, 36, 39, 42, 45, 48, 51
6. Count by 5s. 50, 55, 60, 65, 70, 75, 80, 85
7. Count by 10s. 30, 40, 50, 60, 70, 80, 90, 100
8. Count backward by 2s. 40, 38, 36, 34, 32, 30, 28
9. Count backward by 3s. 30, 27, 24, 21, 18, 15, 12
10. Count backward by 5s. 100, 95, 90, 85, 80, 75, 70
11. Count backward by 10s. 80, 70, 60, 50, 40, 30, 20

32 Use with Lesson 3-8.

© Pearson Education, Inc. 2

16

Name _____

Even and Odd Numbers
R 3-9

An **even** number of things can be matched.

An **odd** number of things cannot be matched.

Draw lines.
☐☐☐
☐☐☐

Draw lines.
☐☐☐☐
☐☐☐

Do the cubes match?

6 is an _even_ number.

Do the cubes match?

7 is an _odd_ number.

Draw lines. Is the number even or odd?

1. ☐☐☐☐☐
   ☐☐☐☐☐

10 is an _even_ number.

2. ☐☐☐☐☐☐☐☐
   ☐☐☐☐☐☐☐

15 is an _odd_ number.

3. ☐☐☐☐☐
   ☐☐☐☐

9 is an _odd_ number.

4. ☐☐☐☐☐☐
   ☐☐☐☐☐☐

12 is an _even_ number.

Write even or odd.

5. 19 _odd_   23 _odd_   20 _even_

6. 34 _even_   14 _even_   27 _odd_

Use with Lesson 3-9. **33**

Name _____

Even and Odd Numbers
P 3-9

1. Circle the odd numbers.

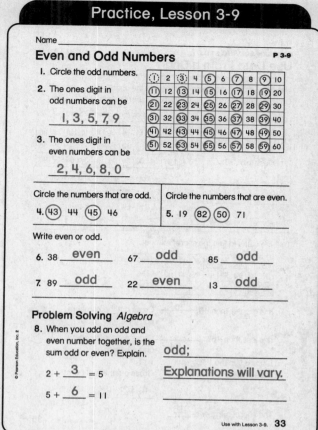

2. The ones digit in odd numbers can be

   _1, 3, 5, 7, 9_

3. The ones digit in even numbers can be

   _2, 4, 6, 8, 0_

Circle the numbers that are odd.	Circle the numbers that are even.
4. (43) 44 (45) 46	**5.** 19 (82) (50) 71

Write even or odd.

6. 38 _even_   67 _odd_   85 _odd_

7. 89 _odd_   22 _even_   13 _odd_

Problem Solving *Algebra*

8. When you add an odd and even number together, is the sum odd or even? Explain.

   odd;

   Explanations will vary.

   2 + _3_ = 5

   5 + _6_ = 11

Use with Lesson 3-9. **33**

Name _____

Ordinal Numbers Through Twentieth
R 3-10

Sometimes we need to tell the **order** of things. We use **ordinal numbers** to tell the order.

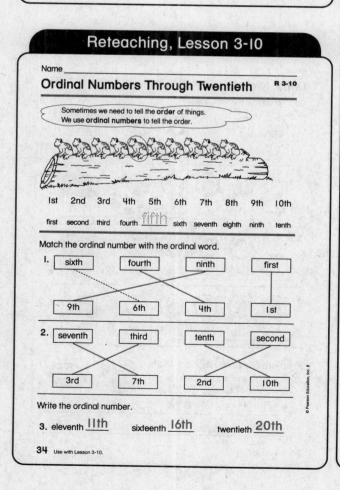

1st	2nd	3rd	4th	5th	6th	7th	8th	9th	10th
first	second	third	fourth	fifth	sixth	seventh	eighth	ninth	tenth

Match the ordinal number with the ordinal word.

1. sixth   fourth   ninth   first

   9th   6th   4th   1st

2. seventh   third   tenth   second

   3rd   7th   2nd   10th

Write the ordinal number.

3. eleventh _11th_   sixteenth _16th_   twentieth _20th_

34 Use with Lesson 3-10.

Name _____

Ordinal Numbers Through Twentieth
P 3-10

Use the crayons to solve.
Write the letter or number.

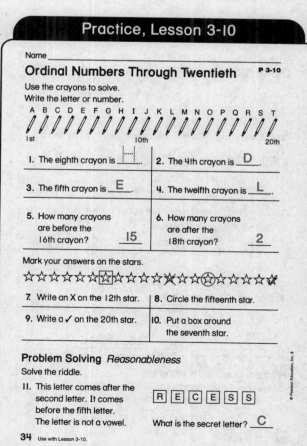

A B C D E F G H I J K L M N O P Q R S T
1st   10th   20th

1. The eighth crayon is _H_.

2. The 4th crayon is _D_.

3. The fifth crayon is _E_.

4. The twelfth crayon is _L_.

5. How many crayons are before the 16th crayon? _15_

6. How many crayons are after the 18th crayon? _2_

Mark your answers on the stars.

☆☆☆☆☆▣☆☆☆☆✳☆☆⊙☆☆☆✶

7. Write an X on the 12th star.

8. Circle the fifteenth star.

9. Write a ✓ on the 20th star.

10. Put a box around the seventh star.

Problem Solving *Reasonableness*

Solve the riddle.

11. This letter comes after the second letter. It comes before the fifth letter. The letter is not a vowel.

R	E	C	E	S	S

What is the secret letter? _C_

34 Use with Lesson 3-10.

Name _____

PROBLEM-SOLVING SKILL   R 3-11

Use Data From a Chart

Use clues to find the secret number on the chart.
Cross out numbers on the chart that do not fit each clue.

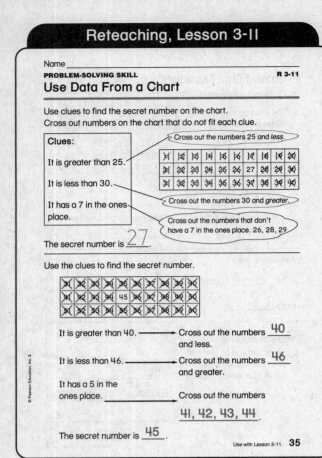

Clues:

It is greater than 25.

It is less than 30.

It has a 7 in the ones place.

Cross out the numbers 25 and less.

Cross out the numbers 30 and greater.

Cross out the numbers that don't have a 7 in the ones place. 26, 28, 29

The secret number is 27.

Use the clues to find the secret number.

It is greater than 40. ⟶ Cross out the numbers 40 and less.

It is less than 46. ⟶ Cross out the numbers 46 and greater.

It has a 5 in the ones place. _____ ⟶ Cross out the numbers 41, 42, 43, 44

The secret number is 45.

© Pearson Education, Inc. 2

Name _____

PROBLEM-SOLVING SKILL   P 3-11

Use Data From a Chart

Use clues to find the secret number.
Cross out the numbers on the chart that do not fit the clue.

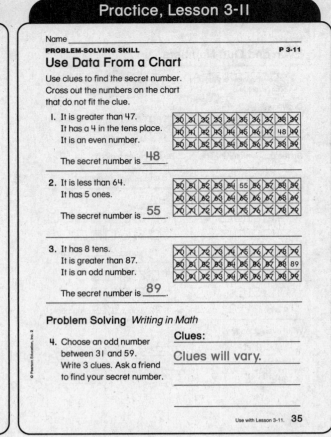

1. It is greater than 47.
   It has a 4 in the tens place.
   It is an even number.

   The secret number is 48.

2. It is less than 64.
   It has 5 ones.

   The secret number is 55.

3. It has 8 tens.
   It is greater than 87.
   It is an odd number.

   The secret number is 89.

Problem Solving *Writing in Math*

4. Choose an odd number between 31 and 59. Write 3 clues. Ask a friend to find your secret number.

   Clues:

   Clues will vary.

© Pearson Education, Inc. 2

Name _____

R 3-12

Dime, Nickel, and Penny

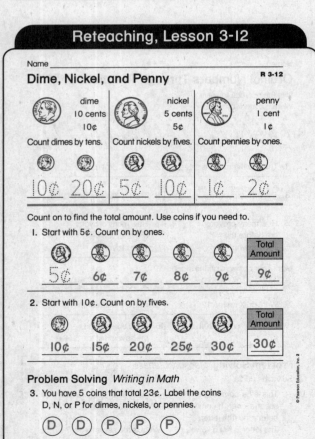

dime 10 cents 10¢	nickel 5 cents 5¢	penny 1 cent 1¢
Count dimes by tens.	Count nickels by fives.	Count pennies by ones.
10¢ 20¢	5¢ 10¢	1¢ 2¢

Count on to find the total amount. Use coins if you need to.

1. Start with 5¢. Count on by ones.

   5¢   6¢   7¢   8¢   9¢   Total Amount 9¢

2. Start with 10¢. Count on by fives.

   10¢   15¢   20¢   25¢   30¢   Total Amount 30¢

Problem Solving *Writing in Math*

3. You have 5 coins that total 23¢. Label the coins D, N, or P for dimes, nickels, or pennies.

   (D) (D) (P) (P) (P)

© Pearson Education, Inc. 2

Name _____

P 3-12

Dime, Nickel, and Penny

Count on to find the total amount.

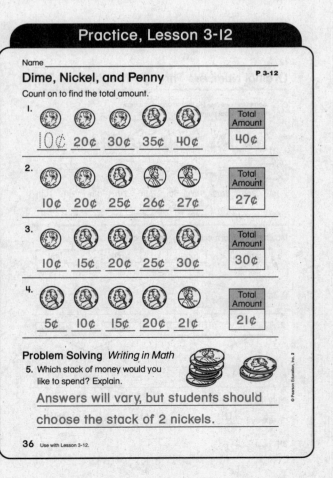

1. 10¢   20¢   30¢   35¢   40¢   Total Amount 40¢

2. 10¢   20¢   25¢   26¢   27¢   Total Amount 27¢

3. 10¢   15¢   20¢   25¢   30¢   Total Amount 30¢

4. 5¢   10¢   15¢   20¢   21¢   Total Amount 21¢

Problem Solving *Writing in Math*

5. Which stack of money would you like to spend? Explain.

   Answers will vary, but students should choose the stack of 2 nickels.

© Pearson Education, Inc. 2

Name _____

Quarter and Half-Dollar

R 3-13

 quarter
25 cents
25¢

 half-dollar
50 cents
50¢

Start with 25¢. Count on by fives.

Think: 25¢   5¢ more   5¢ more

Start with 50¢. Count on by tens.

Think: 50¢   10¢ more   10¢ more

25¢   30¢   35¢   50¢   60¢   70¢

Count on to find the total amount.
Use coins if you need to.

1. Start with 25¢. Count on by tens.

					Total Amount
25¢	35¢	45¢	55¢	65¢	65¢

2. Start with 50¢. Count on by tens and ones.

					Total Amount
50¢	60¢	70¢	71¢	72¢	72¢

Problem Solving *Number Sense*

3. Draw coins so the hand holds half of 40¢.

Answers will vary. The hand should show 20¢.

Name _____

Quarter and Half-Dollar

P 3-13

Count on to find the total amount.
You may use Workmat 6 if you need to.

1.

25¢	50¢	60¢	65¢	70¢	Total Amount
					70¢

2.

25¢	35¢	45¢	46¢	47¢	Total Amount
					47¢

3.

50¢	60¢	70¢	75¢	80¢	Total Amount
					80¢

Problem Solving *Number Sense*

4. Pam has 4 coins in her pocket.
The coins total 50¢.
Color the coins Pam has.

Students should color one quarter, two dimes, and one nickel.

Name _____

Counting Sets of Coins

R 3-14

To count coins, start with the coin that has the greatest value.
Count on coins from the greatest to the least value.

Find the total amount.
Draw an X on the coin with the greatest value.

  Think: 50¢   60¢   70¢   75¢

Start with 50¢.   50¢   60¢   70¢   75¢

Draw an X on the coin with the greatest value.
Count on to find the total amount.

1.

Start with   25¢   25¢   35¢   40¢   45¢

2.

Start with   50¢   50¢   75¢   80¢   81¢

Name _____

Counting Sets of Coins

P 3-14

Draw coins from the greatest to the least value.
Count on to find the total amount.

1.

25¢   50¢   60¢   65¢   70¢

The total amount is _70¢_.

2.

50¢   75¢   85¢   95¢

The total amount is _95¢_.

3.

25¢   35¢   45¢   55¢   60¢

The total amount is _60¢_.

Problem Solving *Estimation*   Answers will vary.

4. Kobe has about 50¢. Circle the coins he might have.

19

Name _____

Comparing Sets of Coins

R 3-15

Which pocket has more money?
Write the total amounts in each pocket and compare them.

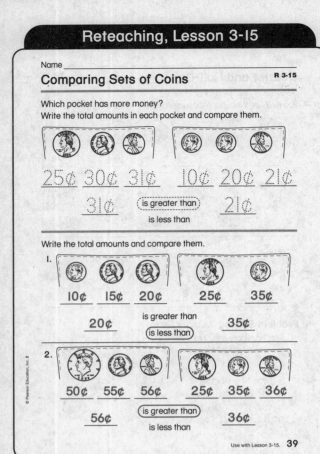

25¢ 30¢ 31¢   10¢ 20¢ 21¢

31¢   (is greater than)   21¢
          is less than

Write the total amounts and compare them.

1.
10¢ 15¢ 20¢   25¢ 35¢

20¢   is greater than   35¢
      (is less than)

2.
50¢ 55¢ 56¢   25¢ 35¢ 36¢

56¢   (is greater than)   36¢
          is less than

Use with Lesson 3-15. **39**

Name _____

Comparing Sets of Coins

P 3-15

Write the total amounts and compare them.
Write >, <, or =.

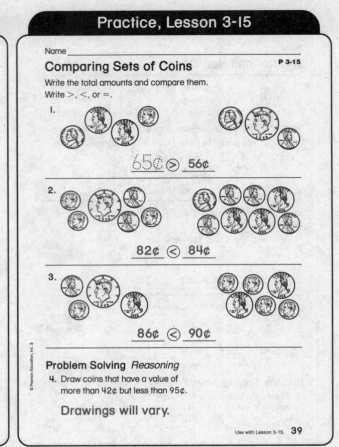

1.
65¢ (>) 56¢

2.
82¢ (<) 84¢

3.
86¢ (<) 90¢

Problem Solving *Reasoning*

4. Draw coins that have a value of
   more than 42¢ but less than 95¢.

   Drawings will vary.

Use with Lesson 3-15. **39**

Name _____

Ways to Show the Same Amount

R 3-16

You can show the same amount in different ways.

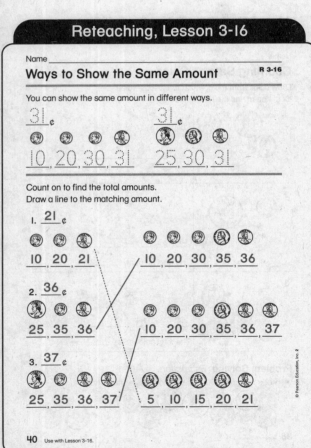

31¢   31¢

10, 20, 30, 31   25, 30, 31

Count on to find the total amounts.
Draw a line to the matching amount.

1. 21¢
10 20 21   10 20 30 35 36

2. 36¢
25 35 36   10 20 30 35 36 37

3. 37¢
25 35 36 37   5 10 15 20 21

Name _____

Ways to Show the Same Amount

P 3-16

Use coins to show the same amount in different ways.
Record with tally marks. Answers will vary. Sample answers are given.

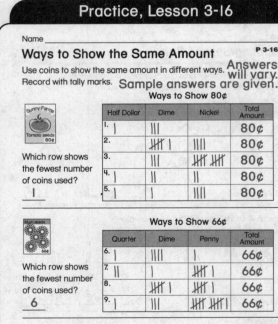

Ways to Show 80¢

	Half Dollar	Dime	Nickel	Total Amount
1.		|||		80¢
2.		|||||	||||	80¢
3.		|||	||||| |||||	80¢
4.		||	||	80¢
5.					80¢

Which row shows
the fewest number
of coins used?

1

Ways to Show 66¢

	Quarter	Dime	Penny	Total Amount
6.			||||			66¢
7.	||			|||||		66¢
8.		|||||		|||||		66¢
9.				||||| |||||		66¢

Which row shows
the fewest number
of coins used?

6

Problem Solving *Reasoning*

10. Jamal has coins in a piggy bank.
    Circle the coin Jamal needs to
    put in the bank to make 75¢.

Name _____

Making Change

R 3-17

A yo-yo costs 34¢.
You pay 50¢.

Start with 34¢

Count on to 50¢

> To **make change**, start counting on from the price until you reach what you paid.

> Now count these coins to find the change.

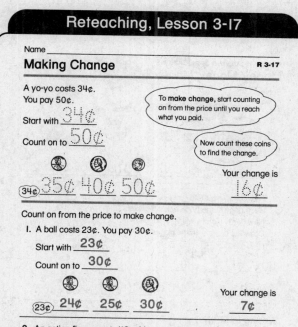

Your change is 16¢

34¢ 35¢ 40¢ 50¢

Count on from the price to make change.

1. A ball costs 23¢. You pay 30¢.

Start with 23¢

Count on to 30¢

Your change is 7¢

23¢ 24¢ 25¢ 30¢

2. An action figure costs 48¢. You pay 60¢.

Start with 48¢

Count on to 60¢

Your change is 12¢

48¢ 49¢ 50¢ 60¢

Name _____

Making Change

P 3-17

Count on from the price.
Draw the coins you would get for change.
Write the amount of change.

Price	You Give	You Get	Change
1. apple 12¢	15¢	12¢ 13¢ 14¢ 15¢	3¢
2. pear 23¢	30¢	23¢ 24¢ 25¢ 30¢	or 7 pennies 7¢
3. pineapple 74¢	90¢	74¢ 75¢ 80¢ 90¢	or 1 dime and 6 pennies 16¢
4. pie 89¢	$1.00	89¢ 90¢ 95¢ $1.00	or 1 dime and 1 penny 11¢

Problem Solving *Algebra*

5. Michael has 34¢.
He needs 45¢ to buy a toy.
Circle the coins Michael needs.
Write the number.

34¢ + 11¢ = 45¢

Name _____

Dollar Bill and Dollar Coin

R 3-18

> A **dollar bill** is equal to 100¢.
> Remember to use a **dollar sign** and **decimal point** when you write $1.00.

100 pennies = 1 dollar

100¢ = $1.00

Circle coins to show $1.00.
Write the number of coins.

1.
_10_ dimes = 1 dollar

2.
_4_ quarters = 1 dollar

3.
_2_ half-dollars = 1 dollar

Problem Solving *Algebra*

4. What 2 coins will make the statement true?

 D N = $1.00

Name _____

Dollar Bill and Dollar Coin

P 3-18

Write each total amount.
Circle sets of coins that equal one dollar.

1.
Total Amount 80¢

2.
Total Amount 90¢

3.
Total Amount $1.00

4.
Total Amount $1.00

Problem Solving *Algebra*

5. Draw the coin that makes each set the same amount.

Name _____

PROBLEM-SOLVING APPLICATIONS　　　　R 3-19

Money, Money, Money

Long ago, coins looked very different in the United States.
Here are some old United States coins.
Count old coins the same way you count coins of today.

1794 silver dollar　　　　　1794 copper cents

Think: $1.00　　+1¢　　+1¢　　+1¢

$1.00　　$1.01　　$1.02　　$1.03

Count on to find how much in all.

1.

$1.00　$2.00　$3.00　$3.01　$3.02

2.

$1.00　$2.00　$2.01　$2.02　$2.03

$2.04　$2.05

Use with Lesson 3-19.　**43**

Name _____

PROBLEM-SOLVING APPLICATIONS　　　　P 3-19

Money, Money, Money

Solve.

1. Count on to find how much in all.

$10.00　　$11.00　　$11.01　　$11.02

2. Rob collects buffalo nickels.
Each page in the book holds 5 nickels.
How many nickels will fill 5 pages?
Draw the nickels on the pages.

_5_　_10_　_15_　_20_　_25_ nickels in all.

Writing in Math

3. Every year, 5 states get their own quarter.
Each state quarter has a different picture on it.
Tell what picture you would draw for your
state's quarter. Draw your quarter.

Drawings will vary.　__Answers will vary.__

Use with Lesson 3-19.　**43**

22

Adding Tens

R 4-1

Name _____

To add tens, count on by tens.

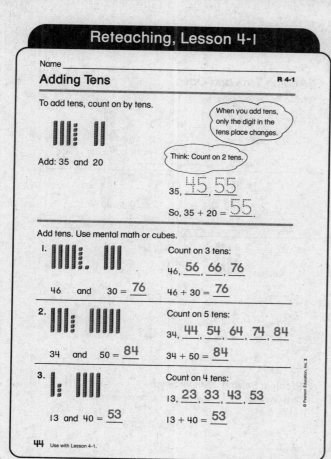

Add: 35 and 20

When you add tens, only the digit in the tens place changes.

Think: Count on 2 tens.

35, $\underline{45}$, $\underline{55}$
$\underline{55}$

So, 35 + 20 = $\underline{55}$

Add tens. Use mental math or cubes.

1. 46 and 30 = $\underline{76}$

Count on 3 tens:
46, $\underline{56}$, $\underline{66}$, $\underline{76}$
46 + 30 = $\underline{76}$

2. 34 and 50 = $\underline{84}$

Count on 5 tens:
34, $\underline{44}$, $\underline{54}$, $\underline{64}$, $\underline{74}$, $\underline{84}$
34 + 50 = $\underline{84}$

3. 13 and 40 = $\underline{53}$

Count on 4 tens:
13, $\underline{23}$, $\underline{33}$, $\underline{43}$, $\underline{53}$
13 + 40 = $\underline{53}$

44 Use with Lesson 4-1.

© Pearson Education, Inc. 2

Adding Tens

P 4-1

Name _____

Add tens. Use mental math or cubes.

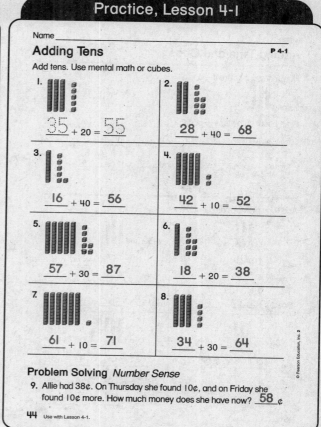

1. $\underline{35}$ + 20 = $\underline{55}$

2. $\underline{28}$ + 40 = $\underline{68}$

3. $\underline{16}$ + 40 = $\underline{56}$

4. $\underline{42}$ + 10 = $\underline{52}$

5. $\underline{57}$ + 30 = $\underline{87}$

6. $\underline{18}$ + 20 = $\underline{38}$

7. $\underline{61}$ + 10 = $\underline{71}$

8. $\underline{34}$ + 30 = $\underline{64}$

Problem Solving *Number Sense*

9. Allie had 38¢. On Thursday she found 10¢, and on Friday she found 10¢ more. How much money does she have now? $\underline{58}$ ¢

44 Use with Lesson 4-1.

© Pearson Education, Inc. 2

Adding Ones

R 4-2

Name _____

Add the ones to make a ten.

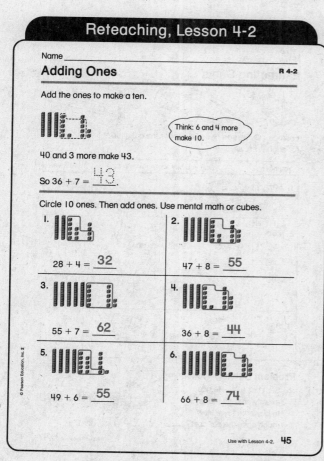

Think: 6 and 4 more make 10.

40 and 3 more make 43.

So 36 + 7 = $\underline{43}$

Circle 10 ones. Then add ones. Use mental math or cubes.

1. 28 + 4 = $\underline{32}$

2. 47 + 8 = $\underline{55}$

3. 55 + 7 = $\underline{62}$

4. 36 + 8 = $\underline{44}$

5. 49 + 6 = $\underline{55}$

6. 66 + 8 = $\underline{74}$

Use with Lesson 4-2. 45

© Pearson Education, Inc. 2

Adding Ones

P 4-2

Name _____

Add ones. Use mental math or cubes.

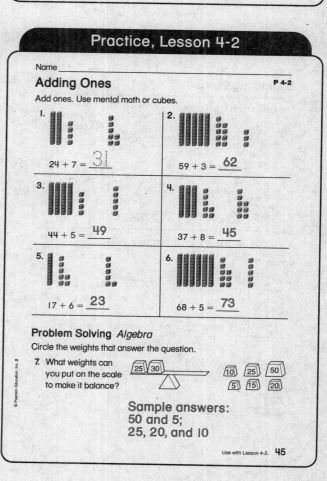

1. 24 + 7 = $\underline{31}$

2. 59 + 3 = $\underline{62}$

3. 44 + 5 = $\underline{49}$

4. 37 + 8 = $\underline{45}$

5. 17 + 6 = $\underline{23}$

6. 68 + 5 = $\underline{73}$

Problem Solving *Algebra*

Circle the weights that answer the question.

7. What weights can you put on the scale to make it balance?

25 | 30   10 25 50
                5 15 20

Sample answers:
50 and 5;
25, 20, and 10

Use with Lesson 4-2. 45

© Pearson Education, Inc. 2

Adding Tens and Ones

R 4-3

Name _____

How many cubes are there in all?

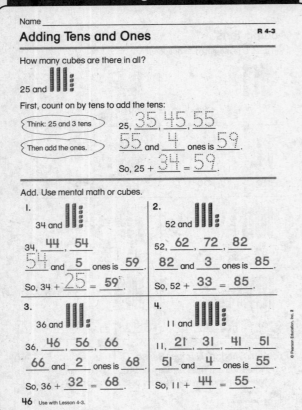

25 and

First, count on by tens to add the tens:

Think: 25 and 3 tens

25, 35, 45, 55

Then add the ones.

55 and 4 ones is 59

So, 25 + 34 = 59.

Add. Use mental math or cubes.

1.
34 and

34, 44, 54
54 and 5 ones is 59.
So, 34 + 25 = 59.

2.
52 and

52, 62, 72, 82
82 and 3 ones is 85.
So, 52 + 33 = 85.

3.
36 and

36, 46, 56, 66
66 and 2 ones is 68.
So, 36 + 32 = 68.

4.
11 and

11, 21, 31, 41, 51
51 and 4 ones is 55.
So, 11 + 44 = 55.

46 Use with Lesson 4-3.

© Pearson Education, Inc. 2

Adding Tens and Ones

P 4-3

Name _____

Add. Use mental math or cubes.

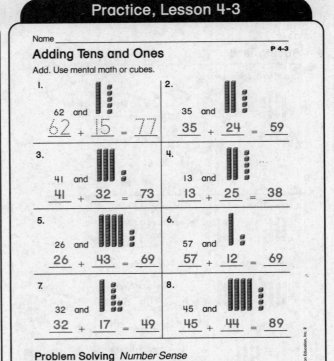

1.
62 and
62 + 15 = 77

2.
35 and
35 + 24 = 59

3.
41 and
41 + 32 = 73

4.
13 and
13 + 25 = 38

5.
26 and
26 + 43 = 69

6.
57 and
57 + 12 = 69

7.
32 and
32 + 17 = 49

8.
45 and
45 + 44 = 89

Problem Solving *Number Sense*

Circle the ones digit to make the number sentence true.

9. 35 + 2▢ = 59
   3   (4)   5

10. 4▢ + 36 = 78
    (2)   4   6

46 Use with Lesson 4-3.

© Pearson Education, Inc. 2

Estimating Sums

R 4-4

Name _____

Use mental math to **estimate**.

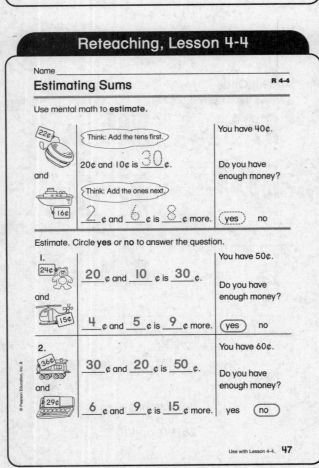

22¢

Think: Add the tens first.

20¢ and 10¢ is 30¢

and

16¢

Think: Add the ones next.

2¢ and 6¢ is 8¢ more.

You have 40¢.

Do you have enough money?

(yes)   no

Estimate. Circle **yes** or **no** to answer the question.

1.
24¢
and
15¢

20¢ and 10¢ is 30¢

4¢ and 5¢ is 9¢ more.

You have 50¢.

Do you have enough money?

(yes)   no

2.
36¢
and
29¢

30¢ and 20¢ is 50¢

6¢ and 9¢ is 15¢ more.

You have 60¢.

Do you have enough money?

yes   (no)

Use with Lesson 4-4. **47**

© Pearson Education, Inc. 2

Estimating Sums

P 4-4

Name _____

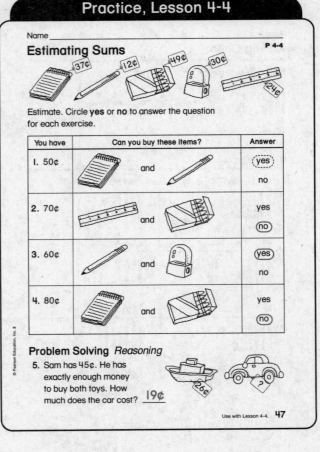

37¢   12¢   49¢   30¢   24¢

Estimate. Circle **yes** or **no** to answer the question for each exercise.

You have	Can you buy these items?	Answer
1. 50¢	and	(yes) / no
2. 70¢	and	yes / (no)
3. 60¢	and	(yes) / no
4. 80¢	and	yes / (no)

Problem Solving *Reasoning*

5. Sam has 45¢. He has exactly enough money to buy both toys. How much does the car cost? 19¢

26¢

Use with Lesson 4-4. **47**

© Pearson Education, Inc. 2

24

Name _____

Subtracting Tens
R 4-5

Use tens and ones blocks to subtract tens.

Think: Count back 3 tens.

When you subtract tens, only the digit in the tens place changes.

Subtract:
57 take away 30

57, _47_, _37_, _27_

So, 57 − 30 = _27_.

Count back to subtract tens. Use mental math or cubes.

1. 64 take away 30
Count back 3 tens.

64, _54_, _44_, _34_

64 − 30 = _34_

2. 49 take away 20
Count back 2 tens.

49, _39_, _29_

49 − 20 = _29_

3. 72 take away 50
Count back 5 tens.

72, _62_, _52_, _42_, _32_, _22_

72 − 50 = _22_

48 Use with Lesson 4-5.

© Pearson Education, Inc. 2

Name _____

Subtracting Tens
P 4-5

Subtract tens. Use mental math or cubes.

1. _46_ − 10 = _36_

2. _82_ − 30 = _52_

3. _75_ − 40 = _35_

4. _38_ − 20 = _18_

5. _69_ − 40 = _29_

6. _41_ − 10 = _31_

7. _55_ − 30 = _25_

8. _32_ − 20 = _12_

Problem Solving *Mental Math*

9. Nick has 90¢. He used his money to buy a bat and a ball. How much money does he have left? _20_ ¢

48 Use with Lesson 4-5.

© Pearson Education, Inc. 2

Name _____

Subtracting Tens and Ones
R 4-6

How many are left?

take away 31
First, count back by tens to subtract the tens.

Think: 57 take away 3 tens. 57, _47_, _37_, _27_

Then take away the ones. _27_ take away _1_ one is _26_.

So, _57_ − _31_ = _26_.

1. take away 26

58, _48_, _38_

_38_ take away _6_ ones is _32_.

_58_ − _26_ = _32_

2. take away 43

67, _57_, _47_, _37_, _27_

_27_ take away _3_ ones is _24_.

_67_ − _43_ = _24_

Solve.

3. Pam has 59 marbles. She gives 35 marbles away. How many marbles does Pam have left?

59, _49_, _39_, _29_

_29_ take away _5_ ones is _24_.

_59_ − _35_ = _24_

 © Pearson Education, Inc. 2

Use with Lesson 4-6. **49**

Name _____

Subtracting Tens and Ones
P 4-6

Subtract. Use mental math or cubes.

1. 57 − 14 = _43_

2. 78 − 25 = _53_

3. 64 − 22 = _42_

4. 45 − 32 = _13_

5. 86 − 21 = _65_

6. 39 − 13 = _26_

7. 97 − 46 = _51_

8. 73 − 41 = _32_

Problem Solving *Writing in Math*

9. Draw cubes to show 56 − 23. Describe how you found the difference.

Answers will vary.

© Pearson Education, Inc. 2

Use with Lesson 4-6. **49**

25

Name _____

Estimating Differences
R 4-7

Use mental math to estimate.

You have 40¢.
You buy:

Think: Subtract the tens first.

$40¢ - 20¢$ is $20¢.$

Think about the ones.

Will you have more or less than 20¢ left?

$40¢ - 24¢$ is ~~more~~ (less) than 20¢.

Estimate. Circle **more** or **less** to complete each sentence.

1. You have 60¢.
   You buy: 37¢

   $60¢ - 30¢$ is $30¢.$

   Will you have more or less than 30¢ left?

   $60¢ - 37¢$ is ~~more~~ (less) than 30¢.

2. You have 70¢.
   You buy: 42¢

   $70¢ - 40¢$ is $30¢.$

   Will you have more or less than 20¢ left?

   $70¢ - 42¢$ is (more) ~~less~~ than 20¢.

50   Use with Lesson 4-7.

© Pearson Education, Inc. 2

Name _____

Estimating Differences
P 4-7

Estimate. Circle **more** or **less** to complete each sentence.

1. $70 - 33$ is ___ more / (less) than 40.
2. $90 - 42$ is ___ more / (less) than 50.
3. $50 - 24$ is ___ more / (less) than 30.
4. $80 - 17$ is ___ (more) / less than 60.
5. $30 - 15$ is ___ (more) / less than 10.
6. $40 - 21$ is ___ more / (less) than 20.
7. $60 - 13$ is ___ more / (less) than 50.
8. $70 - 49$ is ___ (more) / less than 20.

Problem Solving *Reasonableness*

Circle the more reasonable estimate.

9. There is room for 60 people on the bus.
   27 people are already on the bus.
   About how many people can still fit on the bus?

   20 people
   (30 people)
   40 people

10. There were 40 people at the movie.
    18 people left. About how many people are still at the movie?

    10 people
    (20 people)
    30 people

50   Use with Lesson 4-7.

© Pearson Education, Inc. 2

Name _____

PROBLEM-SOLVING STRATEGY
R 4-8

Try, Check, and Revise

Read and Understand

Find two numbers with a sum of 28.

12   15   16

Plan and Solve

Try: Find the ones digits that add up to 8.

Check: 12 and 15
2 ones + 5 ones = 7 ones

Revise: 15 and 16
5 ones + 6 ones = 11 ones

Revise: 12 and 16
2 ones + 6 ones = 8 ones

Now check the tens digits for 12 and 16.

1 ten + 1 ten = 2 tens

Look Back and Check

So 12 ones + 16 ones = 28

Does your answer make sense?

Find pairs of numbers with the given sum.

1. Find numbers with a sum of 37.

   16   15   21

   Try: Find the ones digits that add up to 7.

   Check: 16 and 15
   6 ones + 5 ones = 11 ones

   Revise: 15 and 21
   5 ones + 1 one = 6 ones

   Revise: 16 and 21
   6 ones + 1 one = 7 ones

   Now check the tens digits.

   1 ten + 2 tens = 3 tens

   So 16 and 21 is 37.

Use with Lesson 4-8.   51

© Pearson Education, Inc. 2

Name _____

PROBLEM-SOLVING STRATEGY
P 4-8

Try, Check, and Revise

Find pairs of numbers with the given sum.
The sum of the ones digits must be 10.

1. 52   24   18   46 | Numbers with a sum of 70

   52 and 18
   24 and 46

2. 18   39   11   32 | Numbers with a sum of 50

   18 and 32
   39 and 11

3. 23   57   48   32 | Numbers with a sum of 80

   23 and 57
   48 and 32

4. 45   33   15   27 | Numbers with a sum of 60

   45 and 15
   33 and 27

Use with Lesson 4-8.   51

© Pearson Education, Inc. 2

26

Name _____

Addition and Subtraction Patterns

R 4-9

Find the numbers in the pattern:

7, 17, 27, 37, 47, *57, 67, 77*

1	2	3	4	5	6	7	8	9	10
11	12	13	14	15	16	17	18	19	20
21	22	23	24	25	26	27	28	29	30
31	32	33	34	35	36	37	38	39	40
41	42	43	44	45	46	47	48	49	50
51	52	53	54	55	56	57	58	59	60
61	62	63	64	65	66	67	68	69	70
71	72	73	74	75	76	77	78	79	80
81	82	83	84	85	86	87	88	89	90
91	92	93	94	95	96	97	98	99	100

Look at the ones digit.
It is 7 each time.

Look at the tens digit.
It goes up 1 each time.

The pattern is _____*add 10*_____.

Find the pattern.

1. Color these numbers on the hundred chart:
   4, 9, 14, 19, 24, 29, 34, 39.

   Look at the ones. The ones pattern is *4, 9, 4, 9, 4, 9, 4, 9, and so on.*
   Look at the tens. The tens pattern is *0, 0, 1, 1, 2, 2, 3, 3, and so on.*

   The pattern is _____*add 5*_____.

2. Color these numbers on the hundred chart:
   71, 73, 75, 77, 79, 81, 83, 85, 87, 89.

   Look at the ones. The ones pattern is *1, 3, 5, 7, 9, 1, 3, 5, 7, 9, and so on.*
   Look at the tens. The tens pattern is *7, 7, 7, 7, 7, 8, 8, 8, 8, 8, and so on.*

   The pattern is _____*add 2*_____.

© Pearson Education, Inc. 2

Name _____

Addition and Subtraction Patterns

P 4-9

What is the pattern? Write the numbers.

1. 20, 25, 30, 35, 40, *45, 50, 55, 60,*
   65, 70, 75, 80, 85, 90, 95

   What is the pattern? _____*add five*_____

2. 69, 66, 63, 60, *57, 54, 51, 48, 45, 42*
   39, 36, 33, 30, 27, 24, 21, 18

   What is the pattern? _____*subtract 3*_____

Problem Solving *Algebra*

Find the pattern. Write the missing numbers.

3. 30 and 4 is 34.

   40 and 4 is *44*

   50 and *4* is 54

   60 and *4* is *64*

   70 and *4* is *74*

4. 58 take away 5 is 53.

   48 take away 5 is *43*

   38 take away *5* is *33*

   28 take away *5* is *23*

   18 take away *5* is *13*

© Pearson Education, Inc. 2

Name _____

Finding Parts of 100

R 4-10

Find parts for 100.
Draw more tens to make 100.

(Think: Count up to make 100)

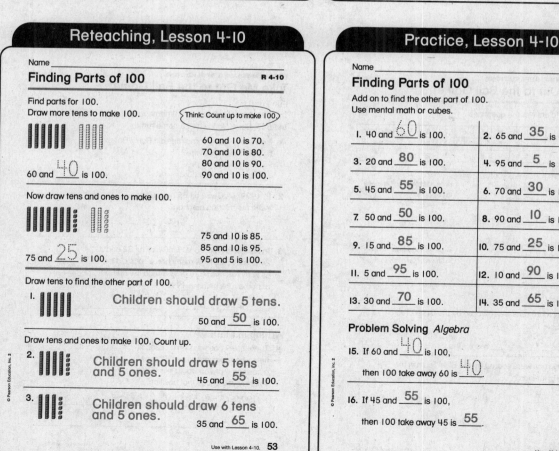

60 and *40* is 100.

60 and 10 is 70.
70 and 10 is 80.
80 and 10 is 90.
90 and 10 is 100.

Now draw tens and ones to make 100.

75 and *25* is 100.

75 and 10 is 85.
85 and 10 is 95.
95 and 5 is 100.

Draw tens to find the other part of 100.

1. Children should draw 5 tens.

   50 and *50* is 100.

Draw tens and ones to make 100. Count up.

2. Children should draw 5 tens and 5 ones.

   45 and *55* is 100.

3. Children should draw 6 tens and 5 ones.

   35 and *65* is 100.

© Pearson Education, Inc. 2

Name _____

Finding Parts of 100

P 4-10

Add on to find the other part of 100.
Use mental math or cubes.

1. 40 and *60* is 100.
2. 65 and *35* is 100.
3. 20 and *80* is 100.
4. 95 and *5* is 100.
5. 45 and *55* is 100.
6. 70 and *30* is 100.
7. 50 and *50* is 100.
8. 90 and *10* is 100.
9. 15 and *85* is 100.
10. 75 and *25* is 100.
11. 5 and *95* is 100.
12. 10 and *90* is 100.
13. 30 and *70* is 100.
14. 35 and *65* is 100.

Problem Solving *Algebra*

15. If 60 and *40* is 100,

    then 100 take away 60 is *40*

16. If 45 and *55* is 100,

    then 100 take away 45 is *55*

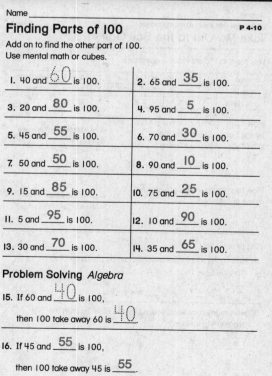

© Pearson Education, Inc. 2

Name _____

Look Back and Check

Pat has 42 stamps.
He gets 20 more stamps.

Now Pat has ⟨62⟩ / 22 stamps.

Check

Think: Which number makes sense?

Pat gets 20 more stamps.

62 is _more_ than 42.

22 is _less_ than 42.

So, Pat has ⟨62⟩ / 22 stamps.

Circle the number that makes sense.
Check if your answer should be more or less.

1. Eric has 67 marbles.
   He gives 20 marbles away.

   87
   Now Eric has ⟨47⟩ marbles.

   Check

   Eric gives 20 marbles _away_.

   87 is _more_ than 67.

   47 is _less_ than 67.

2. Mary has 25 flowers.
   She picks 10 more flowers.

   ⟨35⟩
   Now Mary has 15 flowers.

   Check

   Mary _picks_ 10 more flowers.

   35 is _more_ than 25.

   15 is _less_ than 25.

© Pearson Education, Inc. 2

Name _____

Look Back and Check

Circle the number that makes sense.

1. Vinnie has 30 baseball cards.
   His friend gave him 15 more cards.

   Now Vinnie has ⟨45⟩ / 15 baseball cards.

2. Mary painted 11 pictures.
   Simon painted 8 pictures.

   Together, Mary and Simon painted 3 / ⟨19⟩ pictures.

3. Scott collected 42 coins.
   He put 12 coins in an album.

   There are ⟨30⟩ / 54 coins out of the album.

4. Debbie made 52 puppets for the craft fair.
   She sold 22 of the puppets.

   Now Debbie has ⟨30⟩ / 54 puppets left.

Problem Solving *Visual Thinking*

5. How many cubes are there in all? Circle your answer.

© Pearson Education, Inc. 2

Name _____

Take Me Out to the Ball Game!

Use the chart to answer the questions.

Innings	1	2	3	4	5	6	7	8	9	Final Score
Green Team	3	2	4	5	3	1	2	4	2	26
Blue Team	1	2	2	4	3	1	1	2	1	17

How many more runs were scored
by the Green Team than the
Blue Team in the first inning?

Write a subtraction sentence to compare.

_3_ – _1_ = _2_ more runs

How many runs in all were scored
in the 3rd inning?

Write an addition sentence to find out how many in all.

_4_ + _2_ = _6_ runs

Add or subtract.

1. How many more runs were scored by the Green Team
   than the Blue Team?

   _26_ ⊖ _17_ = _9_ more runs

2. How many runs were scored by the Blue Team in the
   3rd and 4th innings?

   _2_ ⊕ _4_ = _6_ runs

© Pearson Education, Inc. 2

Name _____

Take Me Out to the Ball Game!

Fun Fact!
In 1998, Mark McGwire hit 70 home runs.
In 2001, Barry Bonds hit 73 home runs.

1. How many more home runs did Barry Bonds
   hit than Mark McGwire?

   _73_ – _70_ = _3_

2. In 1999, McGwire hit 65 home runs.
   Write the missing numbers.

   65, _66_, _67_, 68, _69_, 70

3. In his last two seasons, McGwire hit 32 and
   29 home runs. How many home runs did he
   hit in all? Is this more or less than the number
   of home runs he hit in 1998?

   _32_ + _29_ = _61_   _less_

Writing in Math

4. There are 9 positions on a baseball
   field where players stand. Choose
   a position that you would like to play.
   Tell why you chose that position.

   Answers will vary.

© Pearson Education, Inc. 2

© Pearson Education, Inc. **2**

Name _____

Adding With and Without Regrouping
R 5-1

Add 37 + 6.

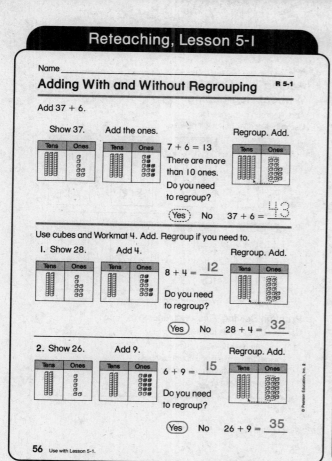

Show 37.	Add the ones.		Regroup. Add.

7 + 6 = 13
There are more than 10 ones.
Do you need to regroup?

(Yes)   No   37 + 6 = __43__

Use cubes and Workmat 4. Add. Regroup if you need to.

1. Show 28.   Add 4.   Regroup. Add.

8 + 4 = __12__

Do you need to regroup?

(Yes)   No   28 + 4 = __32__

2. Show 26.   Add 9.   Regroup. Add.

6 + 9 = __15__

Do you need to regroup?

(Yes)   No   26 + 9 = __35__

Name _____

Adding With and Without Regrouping
P 5-1

Use cubes and Workmat 4.
Add. Regroup if you need to.

	Show	Add	Do you need to regroup?	Find the sum
1.	24	7	_yes_	24 + 7 = _31_
2.	56	9	yes	56 + 9 = 65
3.	92	6	no	92 + 6 = 98
4.	35	8	yes	35 + 8 = 43
5.	69	3	yes	69 + 3 = 72
6.	48	5	yes	48 + 5 = 53
7.	70	4	no	70 + 4 = 74

Problem Solving *Writing in Math*

8. Write 3 different ones numbers you could add to 15 without needing to regroup.
Possible answers: 1, 2, 3, 4

9. Write 3 different ones numbers you could add to 15 where you need to regroup to find the sum.
Possible answers: 5, 6, 7, 8, 9

Name _____

Recording Addition
R 5-2

Add 35 + 7.

Step 1:
How many ones?

5 + 7 = __12__

Step 2:
Regroup 12 as
1 ten and 2 ones.
Write 2 ones.

Step 3:
How many tens?

3 + 1 = __4__ tens

So, 35 + 7 = __42__.

Use cubes and Workmat 4. Add.
Did you need to regroup? Circle **yes** or **no**.

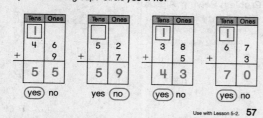

Tens Ones	Tens Ones	Tens Ones	Tens Ones
1 4 6 + 9 = 5 5	5 2 + 7 = 5 9	1 3 8 + 5 = 4 3	1 6 7 + 3 = 7 0

(yes) no   yes (no)   (yes) no   (yes) no

Name _____

Recording Addition
P 5-2

Use cubes and Workmat 4 if needed.
Add. Regroup if you need to.

1.

Tens Ones	Tens Ones	Tens Ones	Tens Ones
3 8 + 5 = 4 3	6 4 + 9 = 7 3	8 2 + 5 = 8 7	1 9 + 7 = 2 6

2.

Tens Ones	Tens Ones	Tens Ones	Tens Ones
2 5 + 7 = 3 2	4 3 + 8 = 5 1	5 6 + 7 = 6 3	9 2 + 4 = 9 6

Problem Solving *Number Sense*

Use the numbers shown. Make the sum of the numbers across equal the sum of the numbers down.

3.   7 5 1 9 3

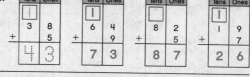

4.   4 7 8 6 5

The order of 6 and 5 may be switched.
The order of 4 and 7 may be switched.

Name _____

Adding Two-Digit Numbers With and Without Regrouping
R 5-3

Add 46 + 18.

Step 1: How many ones?

$6 + 8 = 14$

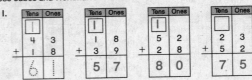

Step 2: Do I need to regroup?

(yes)   no

Step 3: How many tens?

$5 + 1 = 6$ tens

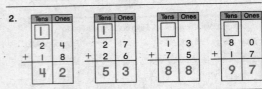

So, $46 + 18 = 64$

Use cubes and Workmat 4. Add.

Tens	Ones
2	4
+ 2	9
5	**3**

Tens	Ones
5	2
+ 1	7
6	**9**

Tens	Ones
3	8
+ 4	5
8	**3**

Tens	Ones
1	7
+ 6	3
8	**0**

Name _____

Adding Two-Digit Numbers With and Without Regrouping
P 5-3

Add. Regroup if you need to.
Use cubes and Workmat 4 if needed.

1.

Tens	Ones
4	3
+ 1	8
6	**1**

Tens	Ones
1	8
+ 3	9
5	**7**

Tens	Ones
5	2
+ 2	8
8	**0**

Tens	Ones
2	3
+ 5	2
7	**5**

2.

Tens	Ones
2	4
+ 1	8
4	**2**

Tens	Ones
2	7
+ 2	6
5	**3**

Tens	Ones
1	3
+ 7	5
8	**8**

Tens	Ones
8	0
+ 1	7
9	**7**

Problem Solving *Reasonableness*

Use the number clues to solve.

3. I am a number between 24 and 34.
You get to me when you count by twos.
You get to me when you count by fives.
What number am I?

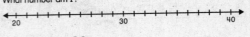

I am the number __30__.

Name _____

Practice With Two-Digit Addition
R 5-4

Remember the steps for adding:

Step 1: Add the ones.
Step 2: Regroup if you need to.
Step 3: Add the tens.

$34 + 27 = ?$

Regroup 11 ones as 1 ten and 1 one.

	Tens	Ones
	3	4
+	2	7
	6	**1**

$12 + 36 = ?$

You do not need to regroup 8 ones.

	Tens	Ones
	1	2
+	3	6
	4	**8**

Write the addition problem. Find the sum.

1.

15 + 26

Tens	Ones
1	5
+ 2	6
4	**1**

32 + 24

Tens	Ones
3	2
+ 2	4
5	**6**

28 + 15

Tens	Ones
2	8
+ 1	5
4	**3**

49 + 13

Tens	Ones
4	9
+ 1	3
6	**2**

Problem Solving *Algebra*

2. Begin with 39. Find the number that gives you a sum of 56. Use cubes to help.

The number is __17__.

Tens	Ones
3	9
+ 1	7
5	6

Name _____

Practice with Two-Digit Addition
P 5-4

Write the addition problem. Find the sum.

1.

34 + 29

Tens	Ones
3	4
+ 2	9
6	**3**

15 + 34

Tens	Ones
1	5
+ 3	4
4	**9**

25 + 48

Tens	Ones
2	5
+ 4	8
7	**3**

36 + 30

Tens	Ones
3	6
+ 3	0
6	**6**

2.

56 + 29

Tens	Ones
5	6
+ 2	9
8	**5**

45 + 25

Tens	Ones
4	5
+ 2	5
7	**0**

36 + 17

Tens	Ones
3	6
+ 1	7
5	**3**

34 + 57

Tens	Ones
3	4
+ 5	7
9	**1**

Problem Solving *Algebra*

3. Write the missing number in each box. You will need to regroup when you add.

4	5
+ 2	**7**
7	2

3	2
+ 1	**9**
5	1

© Pearson Education, Inc. 2

30

Name _____

Adding Money

R 5-5

Adding money is the same as adding two-digit numbers.

Add two-digit numbers.

Tens	Ones
3	5
+ 2	8
6	3

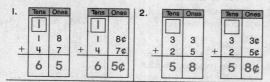

Add money.

Tens	Ones
3	5¢
+ 2	8¢
6	3¢

Remember to write the ¢ sign in your answer.

Add to find the total amount.

1.

Tens	Ones
1	
1	8
+ 4	7
6	5

Tens	Ones
1	
1	8¢
+ 4	7¢
6	5¢

2.

Tens	Ones
3	3
+ 2	5
5	8

Tens	Ones
3	3¢
+ 2	5¢
5	8¢

Problem Solving *Visual Thinking*

3. Sarah spends 25¢ on an apple. Sarah has 60¢. Does she have enough ¢ to buy juice for 39¢ too? Circle **yes** or **no**.

yes   (no)

25¢

+ 39¢

64 ¢

60 Use with Lesson 5-5.

Name _____

Adding Money

P 5-5

Add to find the total amount.

1.

1 7¢	2 4¢	6 8¢	4 4¢
+ 4 5¢	+ 1 9¢	+ 2 2¢	+ 1 5¢
62¢	43¢	90¢	59¢

2.

5 2¢	1 4¢	2 8¢	6 2¢
+ 2 7¢	+ 6 9¢	+ 1 9¢	+ 2 6¢
79¢	83¢	47¢	88¢

3.

4 5¢	2 5¢	1 7¢	6 1¢
+ 2 6¢	+ 3 1¢	+ 4 4¢	+ 2 9¢
71¢	56¢	61¢	90¢

Problem Solving *Visual Thinking*

4. Jessie has 35¢. He wants to spend all of his money. Which 2 pieces of fruit can he buy? Circle them.

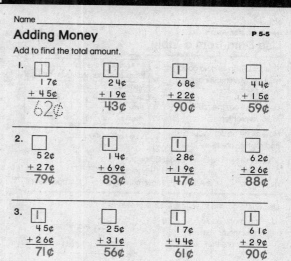

23¢   11¢   12¢   9¢   16¢

60 Use with Lesson 5-5.

Name _____

Adding Three Numbers

R 5-6

Remember you can add in any order. Try different ways to add.

Look for doubles facts. Add the doubles first.

1 4
3 5
+ 2 4
7 3

4 + 4 = 8
8 + 5 = 13

Count on 1, 2, or 3.

5 3
1 9
+ 2 2
9 4

9 + 3 = 12
12 + 2 = 14

Make a ten fact. Look for a ten first.

1 3
2 6
+ 2 4
6 3

6 + 4 = 10
10 + 3 = 13

1. Add.
Look for doubles.

1 1
3 5
+ 2 5
7 1

2 6
2 2
+ 1 6
6 4

2. Add.
Count on.

3 2
1 7
+ 2 4
7 3

4 0
2 9
+ 1 2
8 1

3. Add.
Make a ten.

1 5
2 8
+ 2 2
6 5

1 7
2 3
+ 1 2
5 2

Use with Lesson 5-6. **61**

Name _____

Adding Three Numbers

P 5-6

Add in any order.

1.

4 5	1 6	2 3	3 6
1 5	2 5	3 7	1 4
+ 2 6	+ 6	+ 1 2	+ 2 6
86	47	72	76

2.

3 1	2 8	3 7	2 8
8	2 5	1 2	4 7
+ 4 4	+ 4 1	+ 1 8	+ 1 3
83	94	67	88

3.

2 9	3 4	5 2	4 3
1 1	7	1 5	2 1
+ 2 2	+ 1 6	+ 2 6	+ 1 3
62	57	93	77

Problem Solving *Reasoning*

| 1 | 2 | 3 | 4 | 5 | 6 |

4. Use the numbers on the cards to write 2 two-digit numbers that have the sum of 78.
Possible answer: 36 + 42

5. Use the numbers on the cards to write 2 two-digit numbers that have the sum of 83.
Possible answer: 51 + 32

Use with Lesson 5-6. **61**

Name _____

PROBLEM-SOLVING SKILL   R 5-7

Use Data from a Table

This table shows data about how many animal books are in the library.

Animal Books in the Library	
Kinds of Books	Number of Books
Mammals	42
Birds	28
Insects	14
Reptiles	33

Use data from the table to solve problems.

How many books about birds and reptiles are there in all?

Do I add or subtract?

What numbers do I use in the chart?

Birds: 28 books
Insects: 14 books
Add to find how many in all.

$$\begin{array}{r} 28 \\ + 14 \\ \hline 42 \end{array}$$ books in all

Use data from the table to solve the problems.

1. How many books about mammals and reptiles are there in all?

   What numbers do I use?

   $$\begin{array}{r} 42 \text{ mammals} \\ + 33 \text{ reptiles} \\ \hline 75 \text{ books in all} \end{array}$$

2. How many books about birds and reptiles are there in all?

   What numbers do I use?

   $$\begin{array}{r} 28 \text{ birds} \\ + 33 \text{ reptiles} \\ \hline 61 \text{ books in all} \end{array}$$

3. How many books about birds, insects, and reptiles are there in all? 75 books in all

62 Use with Lesson 5-7.

Name _____

PROBLEM-SOLVING SKILL   P 5-7

Use Data from a Table

Use the data from the table to solve the problems.

Sports Books in the Library					
Kind	Baseball	Football	Soccer	Hockey	Tennis
Number	47	36	25	33	8

1. How many books about football and soccer are there in all?

   61 books

   $$\begin{array}{r} 36 \\ + 25 \\ \hline 61 \end{array}$$

2. How many books about baseball and hockey are there in all?

   80 books

3. How many books about football, soccer, and tennis are there in all?

   69 books

4. If the library got 18 more books about baseball, how many baseball books would there be?

   65 books

62 Use with Lesson 5-7.

Name _____

Estimating Sums   R 5-8

Remember when you estimate, you find the closest ten.
Estimate 22 + 37.

20 21 22 23 24 25 26 27 28 29 30 31 32 33 34 35 36 37 38 39 40

Step 1:
Find the closest ten.

22
+ 37

22 is closest to 20
37 is closest to 40

Step 2:
Estimate.

22 is about 20.
37 is about + 40.

22 + 37
is about 60.

Step 3:
Add.

$$\begin{array}{r} 22 \\ + 37 \\ \hline 59 \end{array}$$

22 + 37 = 59

Estimate the sum. Then solve and compare.

Find the closest ten.

1.   18
    + 34

18 is closest to 20
34 is closest to 30

Estimate.

18 is about 20
34 is about 30

18 + 34
is about 50.

Solve.

$$\begin{array}{r} 18 \\ + 34 \\ \hline 52 \end{array}$$

18 + 34 = 52

2.   42
    + 13

42 is closest to 40
13 is closest to 10

42 is about 40
13 is about 10

42 + 13
is about 50.

$$\begin{array}{r} 42 \\ + 13 \\ \hline 55 \end{array}$$

42 + 13 = 55

Use with Lesson 5-8. **63**

Name _____

Estimating Sums   P 5-8

Estimate the sum. Then solve and compare.

Find the closest 10	Estimate	Solve
1. 53 + 28 53 is closest to 50 28 is closest to 30	$$\begin{array}{r} 50 \\ + 30 \\ \hline 80 \end{array}$$ 53 + 28 is about 80	$$\begin{array}{r} 53 \\ + 28 \\ \hline 81 \end{array}$$ 53 + 28 = 81
2. 36 + 23 36 is closest to 40 23 is closest to 20	$$\begin{array}{r} 40 \\ + 20 \\ \hline 60 \end{array}$$ 36 + 23 is about 60	$$\begin{array}{r} 36 \\ + 23 \\ \hline 59 \end{array}$$ 36 + 23 = 59
3. 67 + 18 67 is closest to 70 18 is closest to 20	$$\begin{array}{r} 70 \\ + 20 \\ \hline 90 \end{array}$$ 67 + 18 is about 90	$$\begin{array}{r} 67 \\ + 18 \\ \hline 85 \end{array}$$ 67 + 18 = 85

Problem Solving *Estimation*

Circle the best estimate.

4. Brittany has 27 animal stickers. Her brother has 33 animal stickers. About how many stickers do they have in all?

   about 50 stickers

   (about 60 stickers)

   about 70 stickers

Use with Lesson 5-8. **63**

© Pearson Education, Inc. 2

Ways to Add

Name _____

Ways to Add   R 5-9

Use **mental math** to add.
43 + 20
I can count up by tens to add. → 43, 53, 63 → 43 + 20 = 63

Use **cubes** to add.
27 + 18

Regroup 10 ones for one ten. →   27 + 18 = 45

Use **paper and pencil** to add.
45 + 15

$$\begin{array}{r} 1 \\ 45 \\ +15 \\ \hline 0 \end{array}$$

Write 1 ten over the tens column. →   45 + 15 = 60

Use a **calculator** to add.
56 + 29   [5] [6] [+] [2] [9]   56 + 29 = 85

Circle the best way to solve the problem. Then add.

1. $\begin{array}{r} 1 \\ 73 \\ +18 \\ \hline 91 \end{array}$ mental math calculator

2. $\begin{array}{r} 46 \\ +30 \\ \hline 76 \end{array}$ mental math paper and pencil   **Methods may vary.**

3. $\begin{array}{r} 1 \\ 54 \\ +17 \\ \hline 71 \end{array}$ mental math cubes

4. $\begin{array}{r} 34 \\ +23 \\ \hline 57 \end{array}$ mental math paper and pencil

64 Use with Lesson 5-9.

Name _____

Ways to Add   P 5-9

Write the way you will solve the problem.
Then add and write the sum.

| · mental math |
| · paper and pencil |
| · cubes |
| · calculator |

Methods may vary.
Possible methods shown.

1. 28 + 22 = 50
mental math,
paper and pencil

2. 48 + 29 = 77
paper and pencil,
cubes, calculator

3. 53 + 7 = 60
mental math,
paper and pencil

4. 36 + 19 = 55
paper and pencil,
cubes, calculator

5. 60 + 28 = 88
mental math

6. 45 + 25 = 70
mental math,
paper and pencil

Problem Solving *Mental Math*

7. Lisa bought some fruit.
She spent 87¢. Which
two pieces of fruit did
she buy? Circle them.

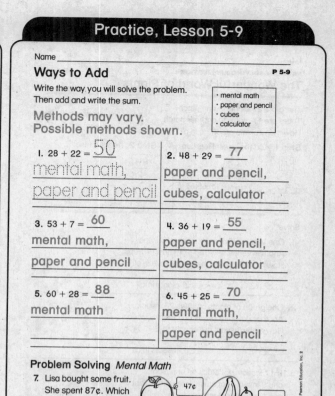

47¢   40¢   37¢

64 Use with Lesson 5-9.

Name _____

PROBLEM-SOLVING STRATEGY   R 5-10

Try, Check, and Revise

Read and Understand

Ken collects animal stickers.
He paid 43¢ for two stickers.
Which stickers did he choose?

Find two stickers that add up to 43¢.

Animal Stickers	
Animal	Cost
Elephant	33¢
Lion	18¢
Tiger	25¢
Zebra	21¢

Plan and Solve

First, pick two numbers: → 25¢ and 21¢
Next, add the numbers: → 25¢ + 21¢ = 46¢
Compare the numbers: → 46¢ does not equal 43¢.

Try again. Pick 18¢ and 25¢. → 18¢ + 25¢ = 43
So, Ken chose the __lion__ and __tiger__ stickers.

Look Back and Check

Are there other pairs of stickers you should check?

Try and check to solve each problem.

1. Nina paid 51¢ for two stickers.
Which stickers did she choose?
__elephant__ and __lion__ stickers

2. Keesha paid 46¢ for two stickers.
Which stickers did she choose?
__tiger__ and __zebra__ stickers

Use with Lesson 5-10. **65**

Name _____

PROBLEM-SOLVING STRATEGY   P 5-10

Try, Check, and Revise

Children bought flowers for school.
What did they buy? Try and check
to solve each problem.

Flower Prices	
Flower	Price
Rose	52¢
Daisy	25¢
Tulip	37¢
Pansy	23¢
Violet	48¢

1. Tammy paid 71¢ for 2 flowers. What did she buy?
__pansy__ and __violet__

2. Rico paid 89¢ for 2 flowers. What did he buy?
__rose__ and __tulip__

3. Katie paid 48¢ for 2 flowers. What did she buy?
__daisy__ and __pansy__

4. Glen paid 85¢ for 3 flowers. What did he buy?
__daisy__ , __tulip__ , and __pansy__

Problem Solving *Algebra*

5. Zack spent 55¢ for two flowers.
One flower cost 30¢. Circle the
coin that shows how much Zack
spent on the other flower.

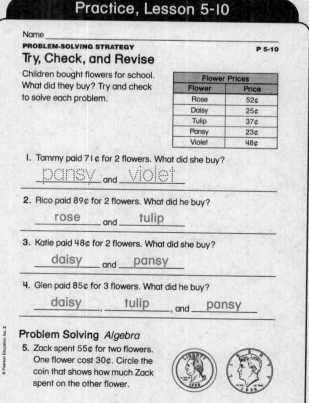

Use with Lesson 5-10. **65**

33

Name _____

The Wonderful World of Plants

There are 26 plants in one patch.
There are 17 plants in another patch.
How many plants are there in all?

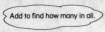 Add to find how many in all.

Step 1: Add the ones. Regroup.   **Step 2:** Add the tens.

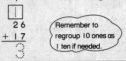

$$\begin{array}{r} 2\,6 \\ +\,1\,7 \\ \hline 3 \end{array}$$

 Remember to regroup 10 ones as 1 ten if needed.

$$\begin{array}{r} 2\,6 \\ +\,1\,7 \\ \hline 4\,3 \end{array}$$

Solve.

1. One Venus's-flytrap plant has 15 traps.
   Another Venus's-flytrap plant has 19 traps.
   How many traps do the plants have in all?

   15 ⊕ 19 = 34 plants in all

2. One group of plants catches 23 insects.
   Another group of plants catches 16 insects.
   How many insects are caught in all?

   23 ⊕ 16 = 39 insects in all

3. If 17 insects got stuck on one plant,
   and 9 insects got stuck on another plant,
   and 5 insects got stuck on a third plant,
   how many insects in all would be stuck?

   17 ⊕ 9 ⊕ 5 = 31 insects in all

Name _____

The Wonderful World of Plants

Fun Fact!
Some meat-eating plants trap animals such
as worms, or even tiny frogs.

Solve.

1. One group of plants traps 17 insects.
   Another group of plants traps 28 insects.
   How many insects in all have been trapped?

   17 ⊕ 28 = 45 insects

2. A plant has 12 traps. Another plant has 13 traps.
   How many traps do the two plants have in all?

   12 ⊕ 13 = 25 traps

3. If one plant can capture one insect in one second,
   how many insects could 25 plants trap in 2 seconds?

   25 ⊕ 25 = 50 insects

Writing in Math

4. Write an addition number story about meat-eating plants.
   Try to use two-digit numbers in your problem.

   Stories will vary. _____

   _____

   _____

Name _____

Subtracting With and Without Regrouping

R 6-1

Subtract 7 from 42.

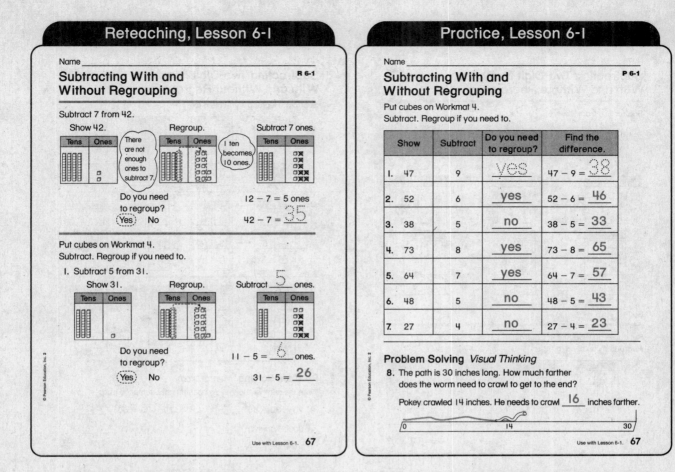

Do you need to regroup? (Yes) No

$12 - 7 = 5$ ones

$42 - 7 = 35$

Put cubes on Workmat 4.
Subtract. Regroup if you need to.

1. Subtract 5 from 31.

Show 31. | Regroup. | Subtract 5 ones.

Do you need to regroup? (Yes) No

$11 - 5 = 6$ ones.

$31 - 5 = 26$

Name _____

Subtracting With and Without Regrouping

P 6-1

Put cubes on Workmat 4.
Subtract. Regroup if you need to.

	Show	Subtract	Do you need to regroup?	Find the difference.
1.	47	9	yes	$47 - 9 = 38$
2.	52	6	yes	$52 - 6 = 46$
3.	38	5	no	$38 - 5 = 33$
4.	73	8	yes	$73 - 8 = 65$
5.	64	7	yes	$64 - 7 = 57$
6.	48	5	no	$48 - 5 = 43$
7.	27	4	no	$27 - 4 = 23$

Problem Solving *Visual Thinking*

8. The path is 30 inches long. How much farther does the worm need to crawl to get to the end?

Pokey crawled 14 inches. He needs to crawl __16__ inches farther.

Name _____

Recording Subtraction

R 6-2

Subtract 8 from 52.

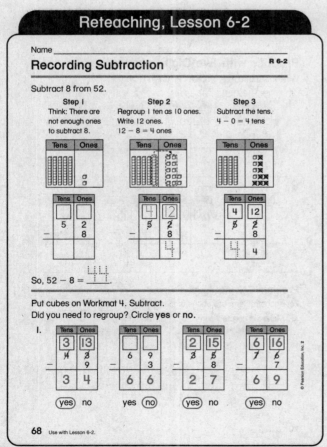

So, $52 - 8 = 44$

Put cubes on Workmat 4. Subtract.
Did you need to regroup? Circle **yes** or **no**.

(yes) no   yes (no)   (yes) no   (yes) no

Name _____

Recording Subtraction

P 6-2

Subtract. Regroup if you need to.
Use cubes and Workmat 4 if you need to.

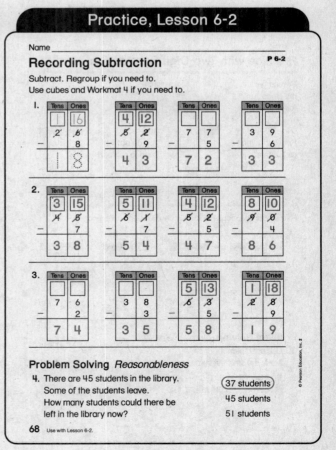

Problem Solving *Reasonableness*

4. There are 45 students in the library. Some of the students leave. How many students could there be left in the library now?

(37 students)
45 students
51 students

35

Name _____

R 6-3

Subtracting Two-Digit Numbers With and Without Regrouping

Subtract 16 from 43.

Step 1
Think: There are not enough ones to subtract 6.

Step 2
Think: Do I need to regroup?

$13 - 6 = \underline{7}$ ones

Step 3
Think: Subtract the tens.

$3 - 1 = \underline{2}$ tens

Tens	Ones
4	3
−1	6

Tens	Ones
3	13
4̶	3̶
−1	6
	7

Tens	Ones
3	13
4̶	3̶
−1	6
2	7

So, $43 - 16 = \underline{27}$.

Put cubes on Workmat 4. Subtract.
Regroup if you need to.

I.

Tens	Ones
3	7
−1	5
2	2

Tens	Ones
4	10
5̶	0̶
−1	3
3	7

Tens	Ones
6	16
7̶	6̶
−2	8
4	8

Tens	Ones
3	15
4̶	5̶
−2	7
1	8

© Pearson Education, Inc. 2

Use with Lesson 6-3. **69**

Name _____

P 6-3

Subtracting Two-Digit Numbers With and Without Regrouping

Subtract. Regroup if you need to.

I.

Tens	Ones
4	13
5̶	3̶
−1	7
3	6

Tens	Ones
6	8
2	1
4	7

Tens	Ones
6	12
7̶	2̶
−3	8
3	4

Tens	Ones
4	13
5̶	3̶
−4	4
	9

2.

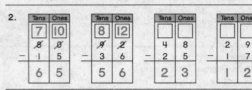

Tens	Ones
7	10
8̶	0̶
−1	5
6	5

Tens	Ones
8	12
9̶	2̶
−3	6
5	6

Tens	Ones
4	8
2	5
2	3

Tens	Ones
2	9
1	7
1	2

3.

Tens	Ones
2	18
3̶	8̶
−1	9
1	9

Tens	Ones
5	11
6̶	1̶
−2	7
3	4

Tens	Ones
7	15
8̶	5̶
−4	6
3	9

Tens	Ones
6	15
7̶	5̶
−4	7
2	8

Problem Solving *Mental Math*

Write the number that makes each number sentence true.

4. $90 - 30 = 80 - \underline{20}$

$80 - 70 = 20 - \underline{10}$

5. $70 - 40 = 60 - \underline{30}$

$60 - 10 = 90 - \underline{40}$

© Pearson Education, Inc. 2

Use with Lesson 6-3. **69**

Name _____

R 6-4

Practice with Two-Digit Subtraction

Remember the steps for subtracting:

Step 1: Look at the ones. Regroup if you need to.
Step 2: Subtract the ones. Subtract the tens.

$54 - 17$
Regroup 1 ten as 10 ones.

Tens	Ones
4	14
5̶	4̶
−1	7
3	7

$38 - 13$
You do **not** need to regroup 8 ones. Subtract the ones and tens.

Tens	Ones
3	8
−1	3
2	5

Remember the steps for subtracting. Find the difference.

I.

64 − 18		37 − 14		45 − 26		73 − 25	

Tens	Ones
5	14
6̶	4̶
−1	8
4	6

Tens	Ones
3	7
−1	4
2	3

Tens	Ones
3	15
4̶	5̶
−2	6
1	9

Tens	Ones
6	13
7̶	3̶
−1	5
5	8

Problem Solving *Number Sense*

2. Use each number once.
Make the smallest sum.

5 3 2 4

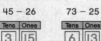 Answer may also be 24 + 35.

Tens	Ones
2	5
+3	4
5	9

© Pearson Education, Inc. 2

70 Use with Lesson 6-4.

Name _____

P 6-4

Practice with Two-Digit Subtraction

Write the subtraction problem. Find the difference.

I.

64 − 39		45 − 16		72 − 31		56 − 29	

Tens	Ones
5	14
6̶	4̶
−3	9
2	5

Tens	Ones
3	15
4̶	5̶
−1	6
2	9

Tens	Ones
7	2
−3	1
4	1

Tens	Ones
4	16
5̶	6̶
−2	9
2	7

2.

84 − 29		34 − 15		96 − 48		43 − 27	

Tens	Ones
7	14
8̶	4̶
−2	9
5	5

Tens	Ones
2	14
3̶	4̶
−1	5
1	9

Tens	Ones
8	16
9̶	6̶
−4	8
4	8

Tens	Ones
3	13
4̶	3̶
−2	7
1	6

Problem Solving *Number Sense*

For each problem, use each number only once. | 1 2 4 5 |

3. Make the greatest sum.

Tens	Ones
5	2
+4	1
9	3

or 51
+42
93

4. Make the greatest difference.

Tens	Ones
5	4
−1	2
4	2

© Pearson Education, Inc. 2

70 Use with Lesson 6-4.

Name _____

PROBLEM-SOLVING STRATEGY   R 6-5
Write a Number Sentence

Read and Understand

Sue has 42 flowers. She gives 15 flowers to her sister.
How many flowers are left?

Plan and Solve

Look for clue words to decide whether to add
or subtract. "How many are left" tells you to
subtract. "How many in all" tells you to add.

Write a number sentence. Use the numbers
in the problem.

$42 \ominus 15 \ominus 27$ flowers left

Tens	Ones
3	12
4	2
− 1	5
2	7

Write a number sentence to solve the problem.

1. Paul has 37 marbles. He gives 18 marbles
   to a friend. How many marbles are left?

   $37 \ominus 18 \ominus 19$ marbles left.

Tens	Ones
2	17
3	7
− 1	8
1	9

2. Tina has 23 crayons. She gets 27 more
   crayons. How many crayons does Tina
   have in all?

   $23 \oplus 27 \oplus 50$ crayons.

Tens	Ones
1	
2	3
+ 2	7
5	0

© Pearson Education, Inc. 2

Use with Lesson 6-5. **71**

Name _____

PROBLEM-SOLVING STRATEGY   P 6-5
Write a Number Sentence

Write a number sentence to solve the problem.

1. Mel's pet store has 52 birds.
   24 of the birds are parrots.
   How many birds are not parrots?

   $52 \ominus 24 \ominus 28$ birds

Tens	Ones
4	12
5	2
− 2	4
2	8

2. Mel orders 47 bags of cat food
   and 38 bags of dog food.
   How many bags does he order in all?

   $47 \oplus 38 \oplus 85$ bags

Tens	Ones
1	
4	7
+ 3	8
8	5

3. There are 78 containers of fish food.
   39 containers of food are sold.
   How many containers are left?

   $78 \ominus 39 \ominus 39$ containers

Tens	Ones
6	18
7	8
− 3	9
3	9

4. The store has 59 dog toys and
   34 cat toys. How many more
   dog toys are there than cat toys?

   $59 \ominus 34 \ominus 25$ more dog toys

Tens	Ones
5	9
− 3	4
2	5

© Pearson Education, Inc. 2

Use with Lesson 6-5. **71**

Name _____

Subtracting Money   R 6-6

Subtracting money is the same as subtracting
two-digit numbers.

5 1¢
− 2 2¢

Think of the pennies as ones
and the dimes as tens.

Tens	Ones
4	11
5	1¢
2	2¢
2	9¢

Remember to write the cents sign in your answer.

Subtract to find the difference.

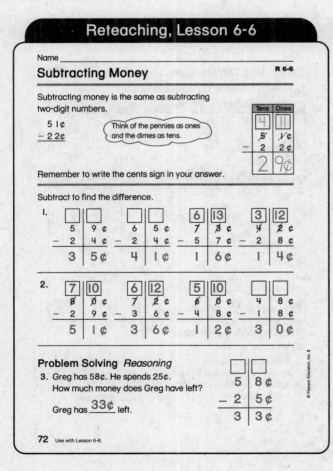

1.
5 9¢	6 5¢	**6** **13** 7 3¢	**3** **12** 4 2¢
− 2 4¢	− 2 4¢	− 5 7¢	− 2 8¢
3 5¢	4 1¢	1 6¢	1 4¢

2.
7 **10** 8 0¢	**6** **12** 7 2¢	**5** **10** 6 0¢	4 8¢
− 2 9¢	− 3 6¢	− 4 8¢	− 1 8¢
5 1¢	3 6¢	1 2¢	3 0¢

Problem Solving *Reasoning*

3. Greg has 58¢. He spends 25¢.
   How much money does Greg have left?

   Greg has **33¢** left.

5	8¢
− 2	5¢
3	3¢

72 Use with Lesson 6-6.

© Pearson Education, Inc. 2

Name _____

Subtracting Money   P 6-6

Subtract to find the difference.

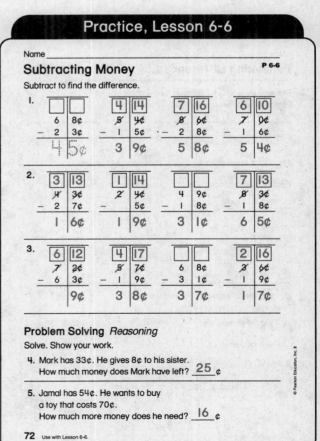

1.
		4 **14**	**7** **16**	**6** **10**
6 8¢	5 4¢	8 6¢	7 0¢
− 2 3¢	− 1 5¢	− 2 8¢	− 1 6¢
4 5¢	3 9¢	5 8¢	5 4¢

2.
3 **13**	**1** **14**		**7** **13**
4 3¢	2 4¢	4 9¢	8 3¢
− 2 7¢	− 5¢	− 1 8¢	− 1 8¢
1 6¢	1 9¢	3 1¢	6 5¢

3.
6 **12**	**4** **17**		**2** **16**
7 2¢	5 7¢	6 8¢	3 6¢
− 6 3¢	− 1 9¢	− 3 1¢	− 1 9¢
9¢	3 8¢	3 7¢	1 7¢

Problem Solving *Reasoning*

Solve. Show your work.

4. Mark has 33¢. He gives 8¢ to his sister.
   How much money does Mark have left? **25** ¢

5. Jamal has 54¢. He wants to buy
   a toy that costs 70¢.
   How much more money does he need? **16** ¢

72 Use with Lesson 6-6.

© Pearson Education, Inc. 2

37

Name _____

Using Addition to Check Subtraction

R 6-7

When you subtract,
you start with the whole.
Then you take part away.
The other part is left.

$$\begin{array}{r} 37 \\ -12 \\ \hline 25 \end{array}$$

Tens	Ones

To check your work,
put the 2 parts back together.
Add. Your answer should be
the whole you started with.

$$\begin{array}{r} 25 \\ +12 \\ \hline 37 \end{array}$$

Tens	Ones

and   and

Subtract.
Check your answer by adding.

1. $\begin{array}{r} 4\ 14 \\ \cancel{5}\ \cancel{4} \\ -1\ 9 \\ \hline 3\ 5 \end{array}$ $\begin{array}{r} 35 \\ +19 \\ \hline 54 \end{array}$

2. $\begin{array}{r} 5\ 13 \\ \cancel{6}\ \cancel{3} \\ -3\ 7 \\ \hline 2\ 6 \end{array}$ $\begin{array}{r} 26 \\ +37 \\ \hline 63 \end{array}$

3. $\begin{array}{r} 7\ 16 \\ \cancel{8}\ \cancel{6} \\ -\ 9 \\ \hline 7\ 7 \end{array}$ $\begin{array}{r} 77 \\ +\ 9 \\ \hline 86 \end{array}$

4. $\begin{array}{r} \boxed{\ }\ \boxed{\ } \\ 3\ 3 \\ -2\ 1 \\ \hline 1\ 2 \end{array}$ $\begin{array}{r} 12 \\ +21 \\ \hline 33 \end{array}$

© Pearson Education, Inc. 2

Use with Lesson 6-7. **73**

Name _____

Using Addition to Check Subtraction

P 6-7

Subtract. Check your answer by adding.

1. $\begin{array}{r} 5\ 12 \\ \cancel{6}\ \cancel{2} \\ -1\ 8 \\ \hline 4\ 4 \end{array}$ $\begin{array}{r} 1 \\ 44 \\ +18 \\ \hline 62 \end{array}$

2. $\begin{array}{r} 7\ 13 \\ \cancel{8}\ \cancel{3} \\ -2\ 9 \\ \hline 5\ 4 \end{array}$ $\begin{array}{r} 1 \\ 54 \\ +29 \\ \hline 83 \end{array}$

3. $\begin{array}{r} 6\ 13 \\ \cancel{7}\ \cancel{3} \\ -3\ 7 \\ \hline 3\ 6 \end{array}$ $\begin{array}{r} 1 \\ 36 \\ +37 \\ \hline 73 \end{array}$

4. $\begin{array}{r} 4\ 8 \\ -2\ 1 \\ \hline 2\ 7 \end{array}$ $\begin{array}{r} 27 \\ +21 \\ \hline 48 \end{array}$

5. $\begin{array}{r} 8\ 14 \\ \cancel{9}\ \cancel{4} \\ -2\ 8 \\ \hline 6\ 6 \end{array}$ $\begin{array}{r} 1 \\ 66 \\ +28 \\ \hline 94 \end{array}$

6. $\begin{array}{r} 6\ 15 \\ \cancel{7}\ \cancel{5} \\ -1\ 7 \\ \hline 5\ 8 \end{array}$ $\begin{array}{r} 58 \\ +17 \\ \hline 75 \end{array}$

Problem Solving *Algebra*

Write the number that makes each number
sentence true.

7. $80 + 10 = 90 - \underline{0}$

$10 + 30 = 70 - \underline{30}$

$70 + 10 = 90 - \underline{10}$

8. $60 - 20 = 20 + \underline{20}$

$50 - 40 = 10 + \underline{0}$

$70 - 20 = 10 + \underline{40}$

© Pearson Education, Inc. 2

Use with Lesson 6-7. **73**

Name _____

Estimating Differences

R 6-8

Remember, when you estimate, you find the closest 10.
Estimate the difference between 49 and 32.

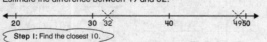

Step 1: Find the closest 10.

Find 49 on the number line.   49 is closest to __50__.

Find 32 on the number line.   32 is closest to __30__.

Step 2: Estimate.   Step 3: Solve.

$$\begin{array}{r} 50 \\ -30 \\ \hline 20 \end{array} \qquad \begin{array}{r} 49 \\ -32 \\ \hline 17 \end{array}$$

49 − 32 is about __20__.

Estimate the difference between 63 and 24.
Then solve and compare.

1. Find the closest ten.   Estimate.   Solve.

63 is closest to __60__.

24 is closest to __20__.

63 − 24 is about __40__.

$$\begin{array}{r} 60 \\ -20 \\ \hline 40 \end{array}$$

$\begin{array}{r} 5\ 13 \\ \cancel{6}\ \cancel{3} \\ -2\ 4 \\ \hline 3\ 9 \end{array}$

© Pearson Education, Inc. 2

74 Use with Lesson 6-8.

Name _____

Estimating Differences

P 6-8

Estimate the difference. Then solve and compare.

Find the closest 10	Estimate	Solve
1. 82 − 36 82 is closest to __80__ 36 is closest to __40__	$\begin{array}{r} 80 \\ -40 \\ \hline 40 \end{array}$ 82 − 36 is about __40__	$\begin{array}{r} 7\ 12 \\ \cancel{8}\cancel{2} \\ -3\ 6 \\ \hline 4\ 6 \end{array}$ 82 − 36 = __46__
2. 51 − 19 51 is closest to __50__ 19 is closest to __20__	$\begin{array}{r} 50 \\ -20 \\ \hline 30 \end{array}$ 51 − 19 is about __30__	$\begin{array}{r} 4\ 11 \\ \cancel{5}\cancel{1} \\ -1\ 9 \\ \hline 3\ 2 \end{array}$ 51 − 19 = __32__
3. 76 − 37 76 is closest to __80__ 37 is closest to __40__	$\begin{array}{r} 80 \\ -40 \\ \hline 40 \end{array}$ 76 − 37 is about __40__	$\begin{array}{r} 6\ 16 \\ \cancel{7}\cancel{6} \\ -3\ 7 \\ \hline 3\ 9 \end{array}$ 76 − 37 = __39__

Problem Solving *Estimation*

Circle the best estimate.

4. Andrew has 68 stickers.
He gives 32 stickers to his brother.
About how many stickers does
Andrew have left?

about 30 stickers

(about 40 stickers)

about 50 stickers

© Pearson Education, Inc. **2**

74 Use with Lesson 6-8.

Name _____

Ways to Subtract

R 6-9

Remember there are 4 ways you can subtract.

Use **mental math** to subtract. 75 − 20

Think: Count back 2 tens to subtract. 75, 65, 55   75 − 20 = **55**

Use **cubes** to subtract. 38 − 12

Show 38. Take away 1 ten.
Then take away 2 ones.

Tens	Ones

38 − 12 = **26**

Use **paper and pencil** to subtract. 60 − 23

Think: Regroup 1 ten as 10 ones.

```
  5 10
  6  0
− 2  3
```
60 − 23 = **37**

Use a **calculator** to subtract. 85 − 59

Press 8 5 − 5 9 =   85 − 59 = **26**

Circle the better way to solve the problem. Then subtract.

1.
```
  7 5
− 1 0
  6 5
```
paper and pencil
(mental math)

2.
```
  4 9
− 2 2
  2 7
```
(cubes)
mental math

3.
```
  6 7
− 1 9
  4 8
```
mental math
(paper and pencil)

4.
```
  8 3
− 3 0
  5 3
```
calculator
(mental math)

Use with Lesson 6-9. **75**

Name _____

Ways to Subtract

P 6-9

Write the letter that tells how
you will solve the problem.
Then subtract and write
the difference.

a. mental math	b. cubes
c. paper and pencil	d. calculator

Letter answers may vary.
Accept reasonable
responses. Possible letter
answers are given.

1.
```
   5 10
   6  0
 − 3  5
   2  5
```
b, c, or d

2.
```
   6  2
 −    9
   5  3
```
b, c, or d

3.
```
  4 9
−   7
  4 2
```
a, b, c, or d

4.
```
   7 13
   8  3
 − 3  7
   4  6
```
b, c, or d

5.
```
  5 3
− 2 0
  3 3
```
a

6.
```
   6 15
   7  5
 − 2  6
   4  9
```
b, c, or d

7.
```
   3 16
   4  6
 − 1  8
   2  8
```
b, c, or d

8.
```
  5 7
− 3 1
  2 6
```
a, b, c, or d

Problem Solving Writing in Math

9. Write 2 new subtraction problems that you
would use pencil and paper to solve.

Answers
will vary.

Use with Lesson 6-9. **75**

Name _____

PROBLEM-SOLVING SKILL

Extra Information

R 6-10

Sometimes there is extra information that you do not
need to answer the question.

There are 4 children on a bowling team. Mike bowls
a score of 65. Sherry bowls a score of 33.
How much higher is Mike's score?

⟨ What is the question asking? ⟩

How much higher is Mike's score than Sherry's score?

⟨ Which information do you need to answer the question? ⟩

Mike bowls a score of 65. Sherry bowls a score of 33.

⟨ Which information doesn't tell about the scores? ⟩

There are 4 children on a bowling team.

```
  65
− 33
  32
```
32 points
32 higher

Cross out the extra information. Then solve the problem.   Solve

1. There are 78 adults at the bowling alley.
   There are 39 children at the bowling alley.
   ~~Mark bowls a score of 82.~~
   How many more adults than children are there?

   39 more adults

```
  6 18
  7 8
− 3 9
  3 9
```

2. In the first game, Sari bowls a score of 57.
   ~~Her brother bowls a score of 48.~~
   In the second game, Sari bowls a score of 38.
   What is Sari's total score for the two games?

   95 points

```
   1
   57
 + 38
   95
```

76 Use with Lesson 6-10.

Name _____

PROBLEM-SOLVING SKILL

Extra Information

P 6-10

Cross out the extra information. Then solve the problem.

1. 45 people ride on the Ferris wheel.
   ~~The Ferris wheel is 38 feet tall.~~
   63 people ride the bumper cars.
   How many more people ride the bumper
   cars than the Ferris wheel?

   18 more people

```
  5 13
  6 3
− 4 5
  1 8
```

2. 26 boys and 32 girls ride the water slide.
   ~~41 adults watch the water slide.~~
   How many children in all ride the
   water slide?

   58 children

```
  26
+ 32
  58
```

3. 72 children are waiting to ride the roller
   coaster. 48 of them get on the next ride.
   ~~The roller coaster has 24 cars.~~
   How many children did not get on the ride?

   24 children

```
  6 12
  7 2
− 4 8
  2 4
```

4. A man sells 53 hot dogs and 87 hamburgers.
   ~~He also sells 45 pretzels.~~
   How many more hamburgers than
   hot dogs are sold?

   34 more hamburgers

```
  87
− 53
  34
```

76 Use with Lesson 6-10.

© Pearson Education, Inc. 2

Name _____

PROBLEM-SOLVING APPLICATIONS   R 6-11

Here Kitty, Kitty!

Subtract to **compare numbers**.

A mother lion has 30 teeth.
Her baby cub has only 14 teeth.
How many more teeth does the
mother lion have?

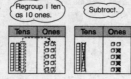

Regroup 1 ten
as 10 ones.

Subtract.

Tens	Ones		Tens	Ones

Step 1
Regroup. Subtract the ones.

```
  2  10
  3   0
-  1   4
       6
```

Step 2
Subtract the tens.

```
  2  10
  3   0
-  1   4
  1   6
```

Solve. Show your work.

1. A tiger is 87 inches long. A lion
   is 76 inches long. How much
   longer is the tiger than the lion?

```
   87
-  76
   11
```
   11 inches longer

2. There are 27 lions in a pride.
   9 of the lions are cubs. How
   many adult lions are in the pride?

```
  1 17
   27
-   9
   18
```
   18 adult lions

3. There are 17 lions in a group.
   10 lions leave the group.
   How many lions are left?

```
   17
-  10
    7
```
   7 lions are left.

Name _____

PROBLEM-SOLVING APPLICATION   P 6-11

Here Kitty, Kitty!

Fun Fact
The cheetah is the fastest animal on land.
It can run up to 70 miles per hour.

1. A cheetah runs at a speed of 70 miles per hour.
   A bus has a speed of 35 miles per hour on a street.
   How much faster is the cheetah's speed than the bus's speed?

   70 $\ominus$ **35** = **35** miles per hour faster

2. There are 22 lions that live in a pride.
   13 of the lions are cubs.
   How many of the lions are not cubs?

   9 lions are not cubs.

3. Estimate how much longer the lion is.

   82 is closest to **80**.

   68 is closest to **70**.

Animal	Length
Lion	About 82 inches
Cheetah	About 68 inches

   So a good estimate of the difference

   would be **10** inches.

Writing in Math

4. Write a subtraction story about cheetahs.

   Stories will vary. _____

   _____

Name _____

Flat Surfaces, Vertices, and Edges
R 7-1

- Flat surface
- 2 flat surfaces meet at an edge.
- 2 or more edges meet at a vertex.

A cube has __6__ flat surfaces.

A cube has __12__ edges.

A cube has __8__ vertices.

A cube has the same shape as a

Circle the object with the same shape.
Write how many flat surfaces, vertices, and edges.
Use solid figures to help you.

1.

A pyramid has __5__ flat surfaces, __5__ vertices, and __8__ edges.

2.

A rectangular prism has __6__ flat surfaces, __8__ vertices,

and __12__ edges.

78 Use with Lesson 7-1.

© Pearson Education, Inc. 2

Name _____

Flat Surfaces, Vertices, and Edges
P 7-1

Write how many flat surfaces, vertices, and edges.
Then circle the objects that have the same shape.

1. A cube has __6__ flat surfaces, __8__ vertices, and __12__ edges.

2. A cylinder has __2__ flat surfaces, __0__ vertices, and __0__ edges.

3. A rectangular prism has __6__ flat surfaces, __8__ vertices,

and __12__ edges.

Problem Solving *Visual Thinking*

Circle the answer.

4. Which shapes could roll if you turned them on their side?

78 Use with Lesson 7-1.

© Pearson Education, Inc. 2

Name _____

Relating Plane Shapes to Solid Figures
R 7-2

If you trace the flat surfaces of this box, you will get these shapes.

Use the solid figures in your classroom.
Trace one flat surface. Draw the shape on the page.

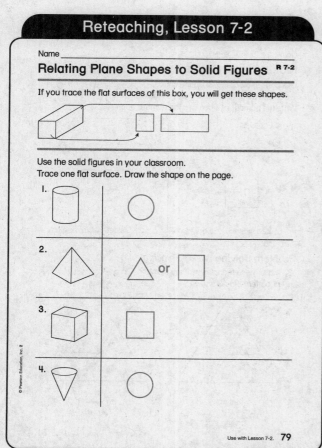

1.

2.   or

3.

4.

Use with Lesson 7-2. **79**

© Pearson Education, Inc. 2

Name _____

Relating Plane Shapes to Solid Figures
P 7-2

Circle the solid figure or figures you can trace
to make the plane shape.

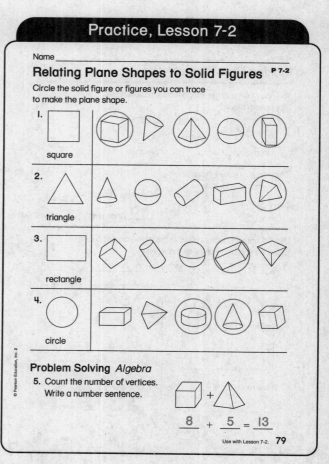

1. square

2. triangle

3. rectangle

4. circle

Problem Solving *Algebra*

5. Count the number of vertices.
   Write a number sentence.

   __8__ + __5__ = __13__

Use with Lesson 7-2. **79**

© Pearson Education, Inc. 2

Name _____

PROBLEM-SOLVING SKILL   R 7-3

Use Data from a Picture

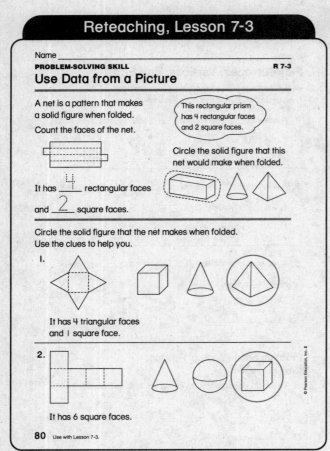

A net is a pattern that makes a solid figure when folded.

Count the faces of the net.

This rectangular prism has 4 rectangular faces and 2 square faces.

It has __4__ rectangular faces

and __2__ square faces.

Circle the solid figure that this net would make when folded.

Circle the solid figure that the net makes when folded. Use the clues to help you.

1.

It has 4 triangular faces and 1 square face.

2.

It has 6 square faces.

80   Use with Lesson 7-3.

© Pearson Education, Inc. 2

Name _____

PROBLEM-SOLVING SKILL   P 7-3

Use Data from a Picture

Circle the solid figure that the net will make if you fold it and tape it together.

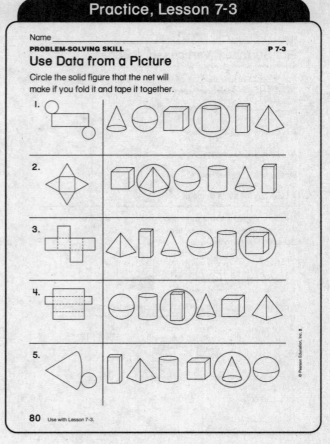

1.

2.

3.

4.

5.

80   Use with Lesson 7-3.

© Pearson Education, Inc. 2

Name _____

Making New Shapes   R 7-4

You can make a larger shape from smaller shapes. Use pattern blocks.

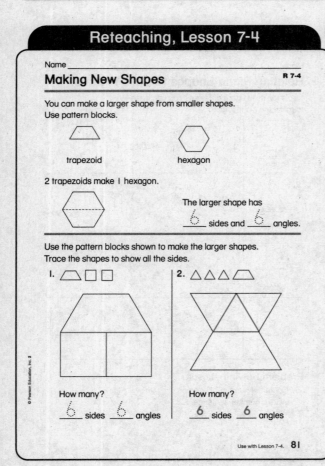

trapezoid   hexagon

2 trapezoids make 1 hexagon.

The larger shape has __6__ sides and __6__ angles.

Use the pattern blocks shown to make the larger shapes. Trace the shapes to show all the sides.

1.

How many? __6__ sides __6__ angles

2.

How many? __6__ sides __6__ angles

Use with Lesson 7-4. 81

© Pearson Education, Inc. 2

Name _____

Making New Shapes   P 7-4

Sample answers are given.

Use pattern blocks to make the shape. Trace and color to show one way to make it. Write the number of sides and the number of angles.

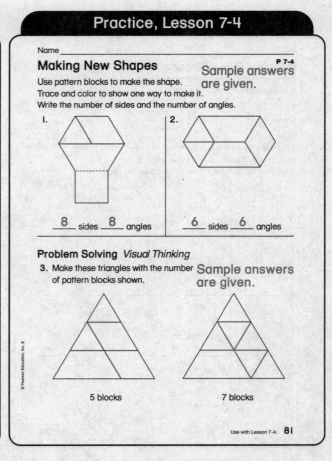

1.

__8__ sides __8__ angles

2.

__6__ sides __6__ angles

Problem Solving Visual Thinking

3. Make these triangles with the number of pattern blocks shown.

Sample answers are given.

5 blocks   7 blocks

Use with Lesson 7-4. 81

© Pearson Education, Inc. 2

42

Name _____

Congruence

R 7-5

These rectangles are not the same shape.

They are not congruent.

These rectangles are not the same size.

They are not congruent.

These rectangles are the same shape and same size.

They are congruent.

Are the shapes congruent? Circle **Yes** or **No.**

		Same Shape	Same Size	Congruent
1.		(Yes) / No	(Yes) / No	(Yes) / No
2.		(Yes) / No	Yes / (No)	Yes / (No)
3.		(Yes) / No	(Yes) / No	(Yes) / No
4.		Yes / (No)	(Yes) / No	Yes / (No)

© Pearson Education, Inc. 2

82   Use with Lesson 7-5.

Name _____

Congruence

P 7-5

Draw a shape that is congruent.

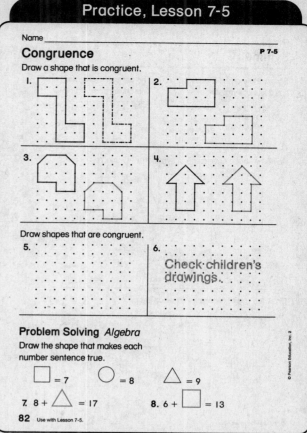

1.

2.

3.

4.

Draw shapes that are congruent.

5.

6.   Check children's drawings.

Problem Solving *Algebra*

Draw the shape that makes each number sentence true.

$\square = 7$ $\bigcirc = 8$ $\triangle = 9$

7. $8 + \triangle = 17$ 8. $6 + \square = 13$

© Pearson Education, Inc. 2

82   Use with Lesson 7-5.

Name _____

Slides, Flips, and Turns

R 7-6

You can slide shapes. You can flip shapes. You can turn shapes.

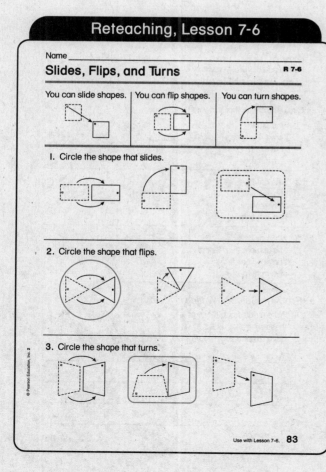

1. Circle the shape that slides.

2. Circle the shape that flips.

3. Circle the shape that turns.

Use with Lesson 7-6. 83

Name _____

Slides, Flips, and Turns

P 7-6

Is it a slide, a flip, or a turn? Circle the answer.

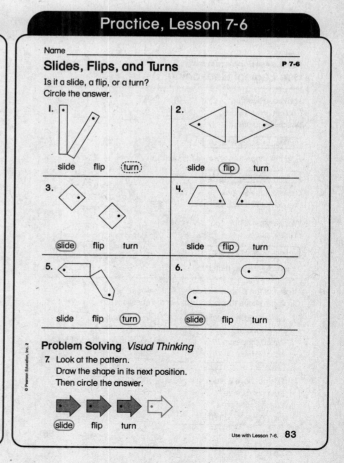

1.   slide   flip   (turn)

2.   slide   (flip)   turn

3.   (slide)   flip   turn

4.   slide   (flip)   turn

5.   slide   flip   (turn)

6.   (slide)   flip   turn

Problem Solving *Visual Thinking*

7. Look at the pattern.
   Draw the shape in its next position.
   Then circle the answer.

   (slide)   flip   turn

© Pearson Education, Inc. 2

Use with Lesson 7-6. 83

Reteaching, Lesson 7-7

Name _____

Symmetry

R 7-7

Both parts match. This shape has a line of symmetry.

The parts do not match. This shape does not have a line of symmetry.

A line of symmetry makes 2 matching parts.

Does the shape have a line of symmetry? Circle **Yes** or **No**.

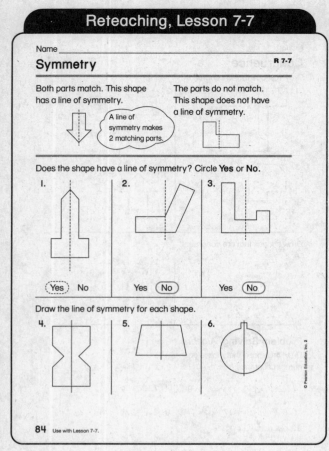

1. (Yes) No

2. Yes (No)

3. Yes (No)

Draw the line of symmetry for each shape.

4.

5.

6.

84 Use with Lesson 7-7.

© Pearson Education, Inc. 2

Practice, Lesson 7-7

Name _____

Symmetry

P 7-7

Draw the matching part to make the shape symmetrical.

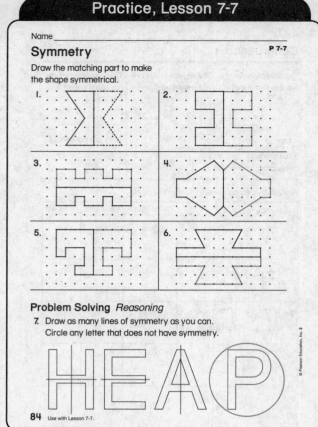

1.

2.

3.

4.

5.

6.

Problem Solving *Reasoning*

7. Draw as many lines of symmetry as you can. Circle any letter that does not have symmetry.

HEAP

84 Use with Lesson 7-7.

© Pearson Education, Inc. 2

Reteaching, Lesson 7-8

Name _____

PROBLEM-SOLVING STRATEGY

Use Logical Reasoning

R 7-8

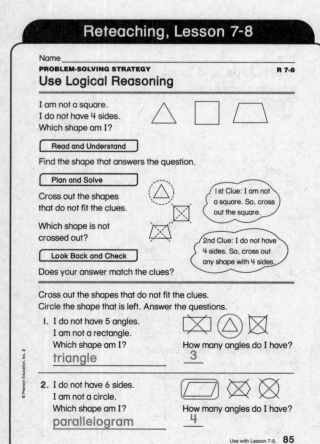

I am not a square.
I do not have 4 sides.
Which shape am I?

⬜ **Read and Understand**

Find the shape that answers the question.

⬜ **Plan and Solve**

Cross out the shapes that do not fit the clues.

Which shape is not crossed out?

1st Clue: I am not a square. So, cross out the square.

2nd Clue: I do not have 4 sides. So, cross out any shape with 4 sides.

⬜ **Look Back and Check**

Does your answer match the clues?

Cross out the shapes that do not fit the clues.
Circle the shape that is left. Answer the questions.

1. I do not have 5 angles.
   I am not a rectangle.
   Which shape am I?

   triangle

   How many angles do I have?

   3

2. I do not have 6 sides.
   I am not a circle.
   Which shape am I?

   parallelogram

   How many angles do I have?

   4

Use with Lesson 7-8. 85

© Pearson Education, Inc. 2

Practice, Lesson 7-8

Name _____

PROBLEM-SOLVING STRATEGY

Use Logical Reasoning

P 7-8

Cross out the shapes that do not fit the clues.
Circle the shape that answers the question.

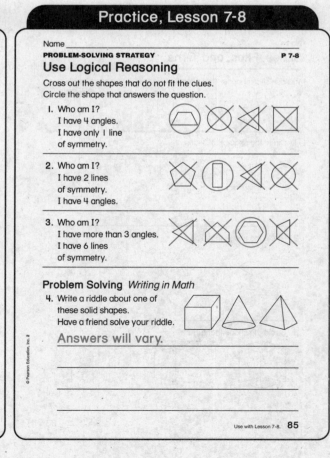

1. Who am I?
   I have 4 angles.
   I have only 1 line of symmetry.

2. Who am I?
   I have 2 lines of symmetry.
   I have 4 angles.

3. Who am I?
   I have more than 3 angles.
   I have 6 lines of symmetry.

Problem Solving *Writing in Math*

4. Write a riddle about one of these solid shapes.
   Have a friend solve your riddle.

   Answers will vary.

   _____

   _____

   _____

Use with Lesson 7-8. 85

© Pearson Education, Inc. 2

44

Name

Equal Parts

R 7-9

Equal parts are the same shape and size.

_2_ equal parts — (halves) thirds fourths

_3_ equal parts — halves (thirds) fourths

_4_ equal parts — halves thirds (fourths)

How many equal parts? Write the number of parts or circle halves, thirds, or fourths.

1. _3_ equal parts — halves (thirds) fourths

2. _2_ equal parts — (halves) thirds fourths

3. _4_ equal parts — halves thirds (fourths)

4. _2_ equal parts — (halves) thirds fourths

5. _3_ equal parts — halves (thirds) fourths

6. _4_ equal parts — halves thirds (fourths)

Problem Solving *Visual Thinking*

Draw lines to show 2 equal parts.

Answers may vary.

86 Use with Lesson 7-9.

© Pearson Education, Inc. 2

Name

Equal Parts

P 7-9

Sample answers are given.

Draw a line or lines to show equal parts.

1. fourths

2. halves

3. thirds

4. fourths

Does the picture show halves, thirds, or fourths? Circle your answer.

5. (halves) thirds fourths

6. halves thirds (fourths)

7. halves (thirds) fourths

8. (halves) thirds fourths

Problem Solving *Visual Thinking*

9. Draw one more line to show fourths.

86 Use with Lesson 7-9.

© Pearson Education, Inc. 2

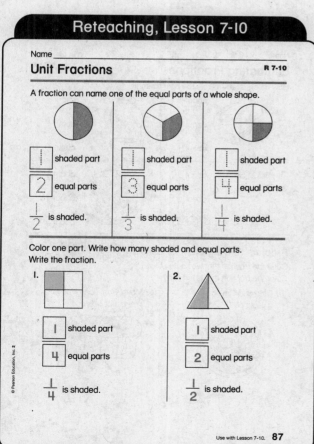

Name

Unit Fractions

R 7-10

A fraction can name one of the equal parts of a whole shape.

_1_ shaded part _2_ equal parts $\frac{1}{2}$ is shaded.

_1_ shaded part _3_ equal parts $\frac{1}{3}$ is shaded.

_1_ shaded part _4_ equal parts $\frac{1}{4}$ is shaded.

Color one part. Write how many shaded and equal parts. Write the fraction.

1. _1_ shaded part _4_ equal parts $\frac{1}{4}$ is shaded.

2. _1_ shaded part _2_ equal parts $\frac{1}{2}$ is shaded.

Use with Lesson 7-10. **87**

© Pearson Education, Inc. 2

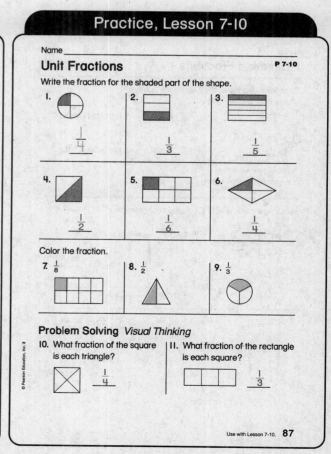

Name

Unit Fractions

P 7-10

Write the fraction for the shaded part of the shape.

1. $\frac{1}{4}$

2. $\frac{1}{3}$

3. $\frac{1}{5}$

4. $\frac{1}{2}$

5. $\frac{1}{6}$

6. $\frac{1}{4}$

Color the fraction.

7. $\frac{1}{8}$

8. $\frac{1}{2}$

9. $\frac{1}{3}$

Problem Solving *Visual Thinking*

10. What fraction of the square is each triangle? $\frac{1}{4}$

11. What fraction of the rectangle is each square? $\frac{1}{3}$

Use with Lesson 7-10. **87**

© Pearson Education, Inc. 2

45

Name _____

Non-Unit Fractions

R 7-11

A fraction can name two or more equal parts of a whole shape.

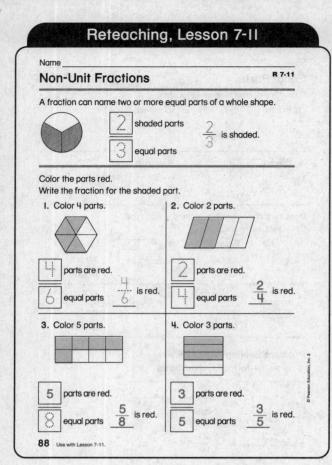

[2] shaded parts
[3] equal parts

$\frac{2}{3}$ is shaded.

Color the parts red.
Write the fraction for the shaded part.

1. Color 4 parts.

[4] parts are red.
[6] equal parts $\frac{4}{6}$ is red.

2. Color 2 parts.

[2] parts are red.
[4] equal parts $\frac{2}{4}$ is red.

3. Color 5 parts.

[5] parts are red.
[8] equal parts $\frac{5}{8}$ is red.

4. Color 3 parts.

[3] parts are red.
[5] equal parts $\frac{3}{5}$ is red.

© Pearson Education, Inc. 2

Name _____

Non-Unit Fractions

P 7-11

Write the fraction for the shaded part of the shape.

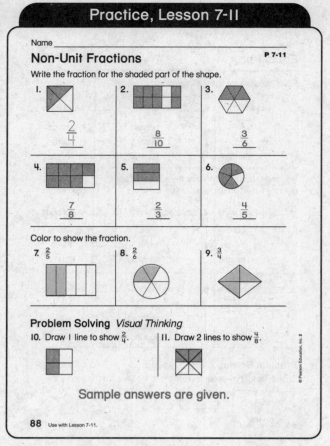

1. $\frac{2}{4}$

2. $\frac{8}{10}$

3. $\frac{3}{6}$

4. $\frac{7}{8}$

5. $\frac{2}{3}$

6. $\frac{4}{5}$

Color to show the fraction.

7. $\frac{2}{5}$ 8. $\frac{2}{6}$ 9. $\frac{3}{4}$

Problem Solving Visual Thinking

10. Draw 1 line to show $\frac{2}{4}$.

11. Draw 2 lines to show $\frac{4}{8}$.

Sample answers are given.

© Pearson Education, Inc. 2

Name _____

Estimating Fractions

R 7-12

To estimate fractions, think about the number of equal parts in the whole.

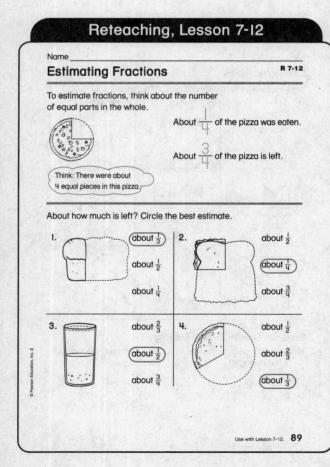

About $\frac{1}{4}$ of the pizza was eaten.

About $\frac{3}{4}$ of the pizza is left.

Think: There were about 4 equal pieces in this pizza.

About how much is left? Circle the best estimate.

1. (about $\frac{1}{3}$)
    about $\frac{1}{2}$
    about $\frac{1}{4}$

2. about $\frac{1}{2}$
    (about $\frac{1}{4}$)
    about $\frac{3}{4}$

3. about $\frac{2}{3}$
    (about $\frac{1}{2}$)
    about $\frac{3}{4}$

4. about $\frac{1}{2}$
    about $\frac{2}{3}$
    (about $\frac{1}{3}$)

© Pearson Education, Inc. 2

Name _____

Estimating Fractions

P 7-12

How much is left? Circle the best estimate.

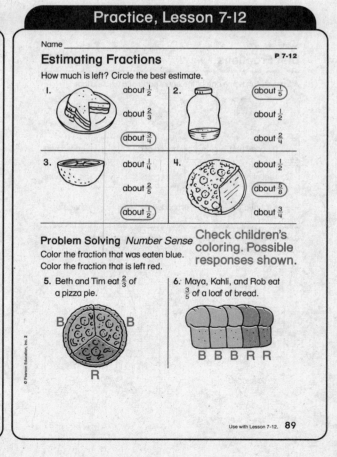

1. about $\frac{1}{2}$
    about $\frac{2}{3}$
    (about $\frac{3}{4}$)

2. (about $\frac{1}{5}$)
    about $\frac{1}{2}$
    about $\frac{2}{4}$

3. about $\frac{1}{4}$
    about $\frac{2}{5}$
    (about $\frac{1}{2}$)

4. about $\frac{1}{2}$
    (about $\frac{5}{8}$)
    about $\frac{3}{4}$

Problem Solving Number Sense

Color the fraction that was eaten blue.
Color the fraction that is left red.

Check children's coloring. Possible responses shown.

5. Beth and Tim eat $\frac{2}{3}$ of a pizza pie.

B   B
R

6. Maya, Kahli, and Rob eat $\frac{3}{5}$ of a loaf of bread.

B B B R R

© Pearson Education, Inc. 2

46

Name _____

Fractions of a Set

R 7-13

A fraction can name the equal parts of a set or a group.

⊕⊕ ⟶ [2] shaded balls $\dfrac{2}{5}$ of the balls are shaded.
○○○ ⟶ [5] balls in all

Color the parts.
Write the fraction for the part you color.

1. Color 2 parts blue.

☆☆☆
☆☆☆
[2] blue stars
[6] stars in all
$\dfrac{2}{6}$ of the stars are blue.

2. Color 3 parts green.

[3] green balloons
[4] balloons in all
$\dfrac{3}{4}$ of the balloons are green.

3. Color 5 parts red.

[5] red apples
[8] apples in all
$\dfrac{5}{8}$ of the apples are red.

90 Use with Lesson 7-13.

Name _____

Fractions of a Set

P 7-13

Write the fraction of the group that is shaded.

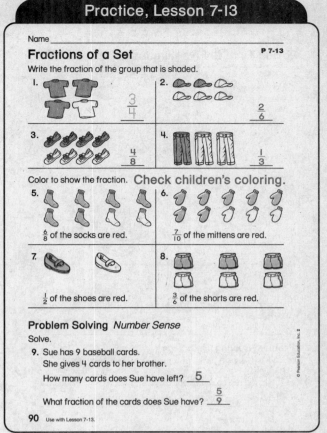

1. $\dfrac{3}{4}$

2. $\dfrac{2}{6}$

3. $\dfrac{4}{8}$

4. $\dfrac{1}{3}$

Color to show the fraction. **Check children's coloring.**

5. $\dfrac{6}{8}$ of the socks are red.

6. $\dfrac{7}{10}$ of the mittens are red.

7. $\dfrac{1}{2}$ of the shoes are red.

8. $\dfrac{3}{6}$ of the shorts are red.

Problem Solving *Number Sense*

Solve.

9. Sue has 9 baseball cards.
She gives 4 cards to her brother.

How many cards does Sue have left? __5__

What fraction of the cards does Sue have? $\dfrac{5}{9}$

90 Use with Lesson 7-13.

Name _____

PROBLEM SOLVING APPLICATIONS

Under the Sea

R 7-14

Some shells have a line of symmetry.
Some shells do not have a line of symmetry.

This shell does not have a line of symmetry.

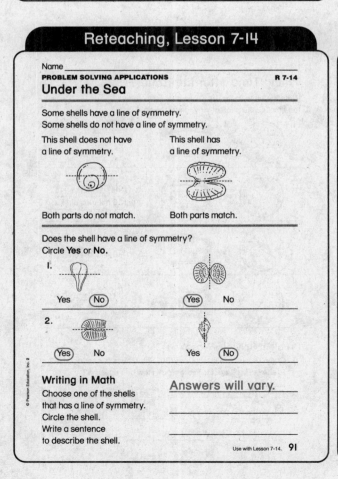

This shell has a line of symmetry.

Both parts do not match.

Both parts match.

Does the shell have a line of symmetry?
Circle **Yes** or **No**.

1. Yes (No)   (Yes) No

2. (Yes) No   Yes (No)

Writing in Math

Choose one of the shells that has a line of symmetry.
Circle the shell.
Write a sentence to describe the shell.

Answers will vary.

Use with Lesson 7-14. 91

Name _____

PROBLEM-SOLVING APPLICATIONS

Under the Sea

P 7-14

1. Here is a type of shell that is found in deep water. This shell can get up to 3 inches long. What shape do you think of when you look at this shell? I think of a

_____ **cone** _____

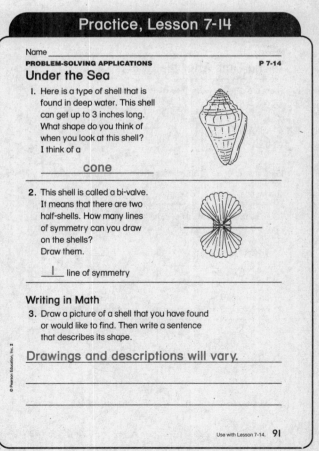

2. This shell is called a bi-valve. It means that there are two half-shells. How many lines of symmetry can you draw on the shells? Draw them.

__1__ line of symmetry

Writing in Math

3. Draw a picture of a shell that you have found or would like to find. Then write a sentence that describes its shape.

Drawings and descriptions will vary.

Use with Lesson 7-14. 91

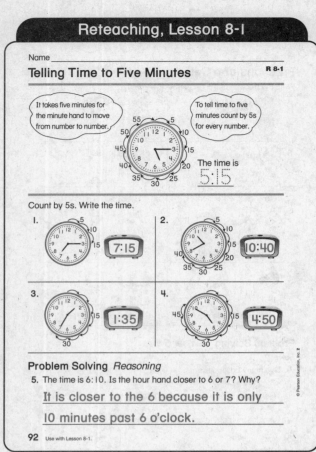

Name _____

Telling Time to Five Minutes

R 8-1

It takes five minutes for the minute hand to move from number to number.

To tell time to five minutes count by 5s for every number.

The time is 5:15

Count by 5s. Write the time.

1. 7:15

2. 10:40

3. 1:35

4. 4:50

Problem Solving *Reasoning*

5. The time is 6:10. Is the hour hand closer to 6 or 7? Why?

It is closer to the 6 because it is only 10 minutes past 6 o'clock.

© Pearson Education, Inc. 2

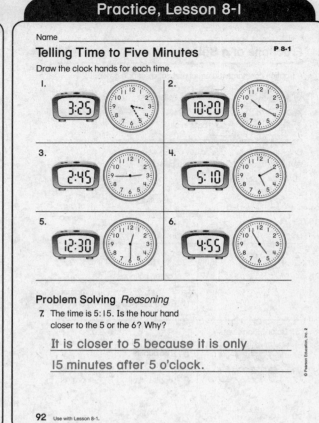

Name _____

Telling Time to Five Minutes

P 8-1

Draw the clock hands for each time.

1. 3:25

2. 10:20

3. 2:45

4. 5:10

5. 12:30

6. 4:55

Problem Solving *Reasoning*

7. The time is 5:15. Is the hour hand closer to the 5 or the 6? Why?

It is closer to 5 because it is only 15 minutes after 5 o'clock.

© Pearson Education, Inc. 2

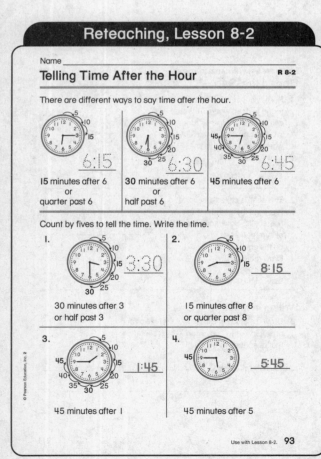

Name _____

Telling Time After the Hour

R 8-2

There are different ways to say time after the hour.

6:15

15 minutes after 6
or
quarter past 6

6:30

30 minutes after 6
or
half past 6

6:45

45 minutes after 6

Count by fives to tell the time. Write the time.

1. 3:30

30 minutes after 3
or half past 3

2. 8:15

15 minutes after 8
or quarter past 8

3. 1:45

45 minutes after 1

4. 5:45

45 minutes after 5

© Pearson Education, Inc. 2

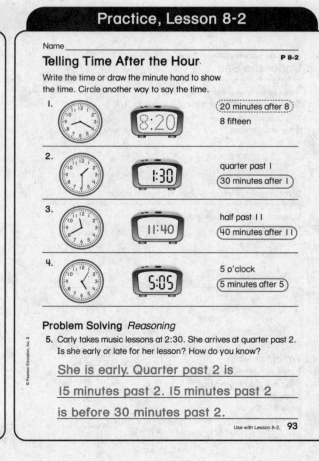

Name _____

Telling Time After the Hour

P 8-2

Write the time or draw the minute hand to show the time. Circle another way to say the time.

1. 8:20

(20 minutes after 8)
8 fifteen

2. 1:30

quarter past 1
(30 minutes after 1)

3. 11:40

half past 11
(40 minutes after 11)

4. 5:05

5 o'clock
(5 minutes after 5)

Problem Solving *Reasoning*

5. Carly takes music lessons at 2:30. She arrives at quarter past 2. Is she early or late for her lesson? How do you know?

She is early. Quarter past 2 is 15 minutes past 2. 15 minutes past 2 is before 30 minutes past 2.

© **Pearson Education, Inc. 2**

Name _____

Telling Time Before the Hour

R 8-3

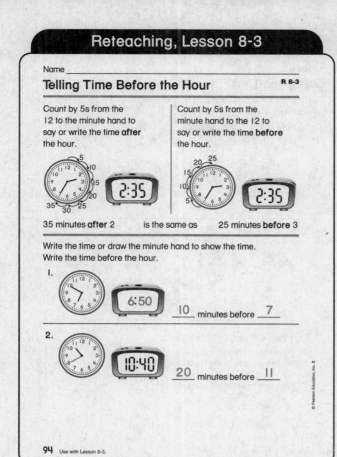

Count by 5s from the 12 to the minute hand to say or write the time **after** the hour.

35 minutes **after** 2

Count by 5s from the minute hand to the 12 to say or write the time **before** the hour.

is the same as   25 minutes **before** 3

Write the time or draw the minute hand to show the time. Write the time before the hour.

1. 6:50   _10_ minutes before _7_

2. 10:40   _20_ minutes before _11_

94   Use with Lesson 8-3.

© Pearson Education, Inc. 2

Name _____

Telling Time Before the Hour

P 8-3

Write the time or draw the minute hand to show the time. Write the time before the hour.

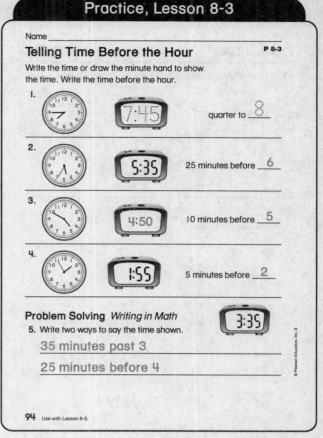

1. 7:45   quarter to _8_

2. 5:35   25 minutes before _6_

3. 4:50   10 minutes before _5_

4. 1:55   5 minutes before _2_

Problem Solving *Writing in Math*

5. Write two ways to say the time shown.   3:35

35 minutes past 3

25 minutes before 4

94   Use with Lesson 8-3.

© Pearson Education, Inc. 2

Name _____

Estimating Time

R 8-4

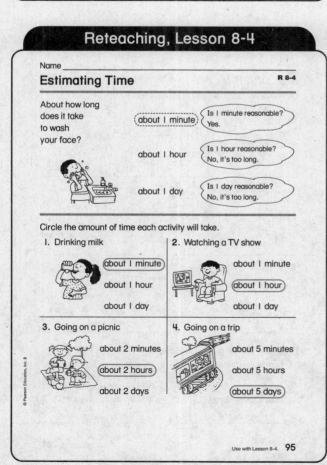

About how long does it take to wash your face?

about 1 minute — Is 1 minute reasonable? Yes.

about 1 hour — Is 1 hour reasonable? No, it's too long.

about 1 day — Is 1 day reasonable? No, it's too long.

Circle the amount of time each activity will take.

1. Drinking milk
about 1 minute
about 1 hour
about 1 day

2. Watching a TV show
about 1 minute
about 1 hour
about 1 day

3. Going on a picnic
about 2 minutes
about 2 hours
about 2 days

4. Going on a trip
about 5 minutes
about 5 hours
about 5 days

Use with Lesson 8-4.   95

© Pearson Education, Inc. 2

Name _____

Estimating Time

P 8-4

Match each activity to the amount of time it would take.

1. Coloring a picture
about 8 minutes
about 8 days
about 8 hours

2. Watering a garden
about 10 minutes
about 10 days
about 10 hours

3. Playing a ball game
about 2 minutes
about 2 days
about 2 hours

4. Making a sandwich
about 5 minutes
about 5 days
about 5 hours

5. Going camping
about 4 minutes
about 4 days
about 4 hours

6. Visiting a friend
about 3 minutes
about 3 days
about 3 hours

Problem Solving *Number Sense*

7. You and a friend play "Pass the Potato." How many times do you think you can pass the potato in one minute? Circle the best answer.

3 times   (30 times)

Use with Lesson 8-4.   95

© Pearson Education, Inc. 2

Name _____

R 8-5

Elapsed Time

Count the number of hours to find out how much time has passed.

Count from the start time to the end time.

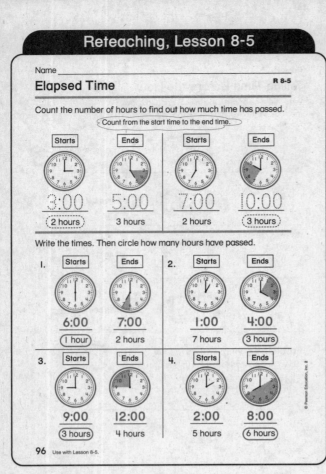

Write the times. Then circle how many hours have passed.

© Pearson Education, Inc. 2

Name _____

P 8-5

Elapsed Time

Draw the clock hands and write the end time for each. Use a clock if you need to.

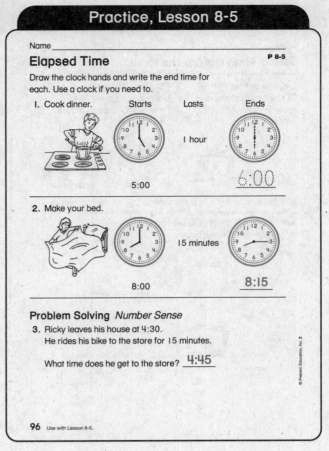

1. Cook dinner.   Starts   Lasts   Ends
   1 hour
   5:00   6:00

2. Make your bed.
   15 minutes
   8:00   8:15

Problem Solving *Number Sense*

3. Ricky leaves his house at 4:30.
   He rides his bike to the store for 15 minutes.

   What time does he get to the store? __4:45__

© Pearson Education, Inc. 2

Name _____

R 8-6

A.M. and P.M.

There are two 12:00s in one day.

12:00 A.M.   12:00 P.M.
Most of us are asleep.   Most of us are eating lunch.

A.M. starts at 12:00 midnight. It ends at noon.
P.M. starts at 12:00 noon. It ends at midnight.

Is it A.M. or P.M.?

3:00 A.M./P.M.   8:00 A.M./P.M.   9:00 (A.M.)/P.M.

Circle A.M. or P.M. to tell the time.

1. 8:00 A.M./(P.M.)   2. 7:00 A.M./(P.M.)   3. 10:00 (A.M.)/P.M.

© Pearson Education, Inc. 2

Name _____

P 8-6

A.M. and P.M.

Draw lines to match the events to the times.

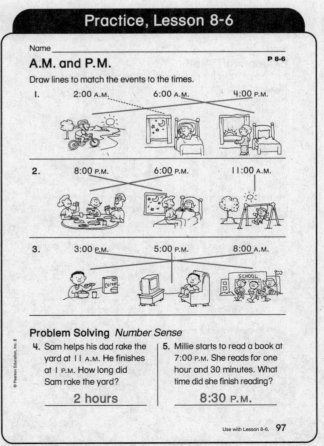

1. 2:00 A.M.   6:00 A.M.   4:00 P.M.

2. 8:00 P.M.   6:00 P.M.   11:00 A.M.

3. 3:00 P.M.   5:00 P.M.   8:00 A.M.

Problem Solving *Number Sense*

4. Sam helps his dad rake the yard at 11 A.M. He finishes at 1 P.M. How long did Sam rake the yard?

   __2 hours__

5. Millie starts to read a book at 7:00 P.M. She reads for one hour and 30 minutes. What time did she finish reading?

   __8:30 P.M.__

© Pearson Education, Inc. 2

Name _____

Using a Calendar

R 8-7

There are 12 months in one year.
March is the 3rd month of the year.

Days of the week — Name of the month

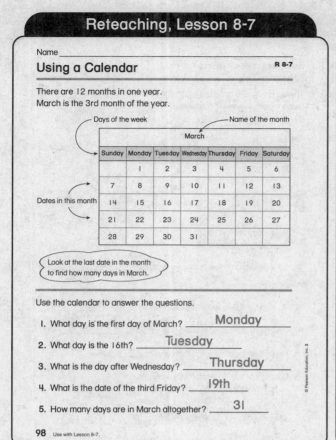

March

Sunday	Monday	Tuesday	Wednesday	Thursday	Friday	Saturday
	1	2	3	4	5	6
7	8	9	10	11	12	13
14	15	16	17	18	19	20
21	22	23	24	25	26	27
28	29	30	31			

Dates in this month

Look at the last date in the month to find how many days in March.

Use the calendar to answer the questions.

1. What day is the first day of March? _____ Monday

2. What day is the 16th? _____ Tuesday

3. What is the day after Wednesday? _____ Thursday

4. What is the date of the third Friday? _____ 19th

5. How many days are in March altogether? _____ 31

98   Use with Lesson 8-7.

© Pearson Education, Inc. 2

Name _____

Using a Calendar

P 8-7

January	February	March	April

(calendar grid for all 12 months)

Use the calendar to answer the questions.

1. What month comes just before April? _____ March

2. How many months have 31 days? _____ 7

3. What month is the ninth month of the year? _____ September

4. What day of the week is December 3rd
   on this calendar? _____ Saturday

5. What date follows June 30? _____ July 1

Problem Solving *Reasoning*

Use the calendar to solve.

6. Sara's birthday is in a month that has 5 Thursdays.
   Her birthday is on a Thursday, and is the
   23rd of the month. What month is her birthday? _____ June

98   Use with Lesson 8-7.

© Pearson Education, Inc. 2

Name _____

Equivalent Times

R 8-8

Equivalent time is another way to say the same time.

Starts   Ends

is **15** minutes   or   one quarter hour

11:45 to 12:00

Starts   Ends

is **30** minutes   or   one half hour

12:00 to 12:30

Starts   Ends

is **60** minutes   or   one hour

12:30 to 1:30

Circle the equivalent time.

1. Mario reads from 12:00 to 12:30.
   (30 minutes)   60 minutes   15 minutes

2. Jamal sings for 15 minutes.
   (one quarter hour)   one half hour   one hour

Use with Lesson 8-8.   99

© Pearson Education, Inc. 2

Name _____

Equivalent Times

P 8-8

Afternoon Schedule	
12:15–12:45	Music
12:45–1:45	Science
1:45–2:00	Recess
2:00–2:15	Story Time
2:15–2:45	Social Studies
2:45–3:00	Clean Up

Use the schedule to answer the questions.

1. Which two activities are one half hour long?

   music and social studies

2. How many hours long is Science? _____ 1 hour

3. Name other activities that are as long as Recess.

   story time and clean up

4. How long are Story Time and Social Studies together?

   45 minutes

Problem Solving *Visual Thinking*

5. Look at each clock. What activity takes place
   between these times?

   _____ music

Use with Lesson 8-8.   99

© Pearson Education, Inc. 2

Name _____

PROBLEM-SOLVING STRATEGY   R 8-9

Make a Table

Sasha had a box of school supplies.
How many of each kind of school supply are there?

Read and Understand

What are the supplies?
How many of each are there?

Plan and Solve

Think: What do I need to find out?

Complete the table. Count the objects.
Use one tally mark for each object.

Look Back and Check

How does the table help you
organize information?

Answers will vary.
Possible response:
Each tally mark in
the table counts as
one item.

School Supplies	
Kinds	Number
Crayons	||
Tape	|
Pencils	⫴⃫
Erasers	⫴⃫ |

Now use the table to answer the questions.

1. How many crayons are there? **2**

2. How many pencils are there? **5**

3. Are there more crayons or pencils? **pencils**

4. How many more erasers are there than pencils? **1**

Name _____

PROBLEM-SOLVING STRATEGY   P 8-9

Make a Table

The second grade class drew pictures of their
favorite pets. Complete the table. Use tally marks.

Favorite Pets	
Rabbit	||
Dog	||||
Hamster	|
Cat	⫴⃫ |
Bird	|||

1. How many children drew
   dogs as their favorite pet? **4** children

2. Do more children like hamsters or birds? **birds**
   How many more? **2** children

3. What pet is the favorite of most children? **cats**

4. Which pet did 1 child name as the favorite? **hamster**

5. How many children are in this class? **16** children

6. What if some children drew these pictures
   as their favorite pets? Draw the tally marks
   there would be for turtles. **⫴⃫ \|\|**

Name _____

Recording Data from a Survey   R 8-10

Take a **survey** to collect information. Information is
called **data**. Make tally marks to record this **data**.

Favorite Frozen Yogurt Flavors

Vanilla	Chocolate	Strawberry
⫴⃫ |	⫴⃫ ||	|||

Use the survey to answer the questions.

1. Which flavor is the favorite of the greatest number of children?
   chocolate

2. Which flavor did the least number of children choose?
   strawberry

3. How many children in all answered the survey? **16**

4. How many more children chose vanilla than strawberry? **3**

Name _____

Recording Data from a Survey   P 8-10

Use the survey to answer the questions.

Favorite Foods	
Food	Number of Children
Spaghetti	⫴⃫ ⫴⃫ ||||
Hot dogs	⫴⃫ ⫴⃫ ⫴⃫ ||||
Cereal	⫴⃫ ⫴⃫ |

1. How many children chose hot dogs? **19** children

2. Which food is the favorite of
   the greatest number of children? **hot dogs**

3. How many more children chose
   spaghetti than cereal? **3** children

4. Which food did the least number
   of children choose? **cereal**

Problem Solving *Number Sense*
Solve.

5. If 7 more children choose spaghetti,
   what will the new total be for spaghetti? **21** children

Name _____

Using a Venn Diagram

R 8-11

A Venn diagram can be used to collect and show information. It can show how many people like different things and how many people like both things.

Do you like hot dogs, hamburgers, or both?

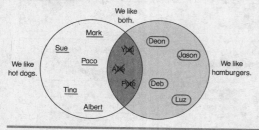

We like both.

We like hot dogs.

We like hamburgers.

Mark, Sue, Paco, Tina, Albert, Yuki, Anne, Pete, Deon, Jason, Deb, Luz

Use the diagram to answer the questions.

1. Draw a line under the names of children who like only hot dogs.

2. Circle the names of children who like only hamburgers.

3. Draw an X over the names of children who like both hot dogs and hamburgers.

4. How many children like hamburgers? __7__ children

5. How many children were surveyed altogether? __12__ children

102   Use with Lesson 8-11.

Name _____

Using a Venn Diagram

P 8-11

Ask 8 children the question below. Record the data using their names.

Do you like cats or dogs or both?

I like cats.   I like dogs.

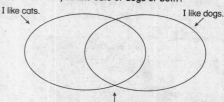

I like both cats and dogs.

Use the diagram to answer the questions. **Answers will vary.**

1. How many children like cats? _____ children

2. How many children like cats but not dogs? _____ children

3. How many children like dogs? _____ children

4. How many children like dogs but not cats? _____ children

Problem Solving *Writing in Math*

5. How can you use the diagram to tell how many children like both cats and dogs?

I can count the number of names in the part of the diagram that overlaps.

102   Use with Lesson 8-11.

Name _____

Pictographs

R 8-12

A pictograph uses pictures or symbols to show information.

Write how many children chose each snack.

Each 😊 = 1 child

There are 9 symbols for popcorn. So 9 children chose popcorn.

Favorite Snacks

Popcorn	😊😊😊😊😊😊😊😊😊	9
Fruit Cups	😊😊😊😊	4
Yogurt	😊😊😊😊😊😊😊	7
Cheese and Crackers	😊😊😊😊😊😊😊😊😊😊	10

Use the graph to answer the questions.

1. How many children like cheese and crackers the best? __10__ children

2. How many children like yogurt the best? __7__ children

3. Which snack is the least favorite? __fruit cups__

4. Which snack is favored by most children? __cheese and crackers__

5. How many more children like yogurt than fruit cups? __3__ children

6. How many more children like cheese and crackers than yogurt? __3__ children

Use with Lesson 8-12.   103

Name _____

Pictographs

P 8-12

Use the graphs to answer the questions.

Favorite TV Show

Animal Stories	🎬🎬🎬🎬 🎬🎬🎬
Sports	🎬🎬🎬
Cartoons	🎬🎬🎬🎬 🎬🎬🎬

Each 🎬 = 1 child

1. Which show is favored by most children?

__cartoons__

2. How many children like Animal Stories best? __7__

3. Which show is the favorite of 3 children? __sports__

Favorite Colors

	😊	
😊	😊	
😊	😊	😊
😊	😊	😊
😊	😊	😊
Red	Blue	Green

Each 😊 = 2 children

4. Which color is favored by most children?

__blue__

5. How many children like red best?

😊 😊 😊 😊
2   4   6   8

Problem Solving *Number Sense*

6. If 4 more children choose green, write a number sentence that tells how many children like green now. Solve.

__4 + 4 = 8__

Use with Lesson 8-12.   103

53

Name _____

Bar Graphs

R 8-13

A bar graph uses bars to show information.
The name of the graph tells the kind of information.

Books We Read Last Summer ← Name of Graph

Count the number of colored boxes and write the number.
These numbers tell how many books each person read.

People Who Read Books: Mick, Raj, Sue, Cory
Number of Books Read: 4, 7, 3, 9

Use the graph to answer the questions.

1. How many books did Mick read last summer? __4__ books

2. How many books did Sue and Raj read last summer? __10__ books

3. Who read the most books? __Cory__

4. Who read the least books? __Sue__

© Pearson Education, Inc. 2

Name _____

Bar Graphs

P 8-13

1. Take a survey. Ask classmates what they like to do inside.
   Make tally marks to keep track of what each classmate says.

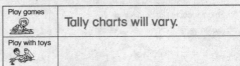

| Play games | Tally charts will vary. |
| Play with toys | |

2. Make a bar graph. Color one box for each
   time an activity was chosen. **Bar graphs will vary.**

Favorite Inside Activities

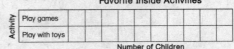

Activity: Play games, Play with toys

Number of Children

Use the graph to answer each question. **Answers will vary.**

3. Which activity is favored by the most children? _____

4. Which activity is favored by the least children? _____

Problem Solving *Writing in Math*

5. Explain how you read the information in the bar graph.

For each activity, count the number of
colored squares in the row to tell how
many children chose the activity.

© Pearson Education, Inc. 2

Name _____

Line Plots

R 8-14

A line plot is another way to show how many.
Look at the parts of the line plot.

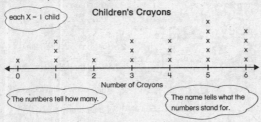

Children's Crayons

each X = 1 child

The numbers tell how many.

The name tells what the numbers stand for.

Number of Crayons

Look above the number 4. There are 3 Xs.

This line plot shows that __3__ children have
4 crayons each.

Look above the number 6. There are 4 Xs. This line plot

shows that __4__ children have 6 crayons each.

Use the line plot to answer the questions.

1. How many children have 3 crayons? __3__ children

2. How many children have 1 crayon? __3__ children

3. How many children have 0 crayons? __1__ child

4. How many crayons did
   the most number of children have? __5__ crayons

© Pearson Education, Inc. 2

Name _____

Line Plots

P 8-14

Use the line plot to answer the questions.

Number of Letters in Our Names

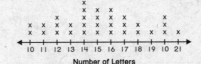

Number of Letters

1. How many children have
   15 letters in their name?

   __4__ children

2. What is the greatest number
   of letters in a child's name?

   __21__ letters

3. How many children
   have 17 or more letters
   in their name?

   __10__ children

4. How many children have
   15 or fewer letters in
   their name?

   __18__ children

Problem Solving *Reasonableness*

Circle the answer that is more reasonable.

5. Susan's last name has fewer
   letters than her first name.
   How many letters are in her
   name in all?

   5 (9)

6. Marshall has more letters in
   his last name than his first
   name. How many letters are
   in his name in all?

   8 (20)

© Pearson Education, Inc. 2

Reteaching, Lesson 8-15

Name _____

Coordinate Graphs

R 8-15

Coordinate graphs show where things are located.

The ordered pair (B, 1) names the location of the fish on the graph.

Where is the mouse?
Start at 0 and go to A.
From A, go up.
Count the spaces.
The mouse is located at (A , 2).

Where is the fly?
Start at 0 and go to B.
From B, go up.
Count the spaces.
The fly is located at (B , 2).

Write the ordered pair where each animal is located.

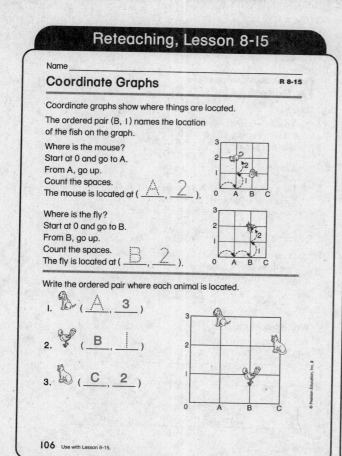

1. (A , 3)

2. (B , 1)

3. (C , 2)

106 Use with Lesson 8-15.

Practice, Lesson 8-15

Name _____

Coordinate Graphs

P 8-15

Find the Wild Animals

Write the ordered pair where each animal is located.

1. (B, 5) 2. (C, 2)

3. (A, 4) 4. (F, 1)

Problem Solving *Writing in Math*

5. Tell how you would find the ordered pair that tells the location of the lion.

Sample answer: Start at 0. Move to A.
Move up 4 spaces to the lion: The ordered
pair is (A, 4).

106 Use with Lesson 8-15.

Reteaching, Lesson 8-16

Name _____

PROBLEM-SOLVING SKILL

Use Data from a Graph

R 8-16

A graph shows us information.

How many animals are there?

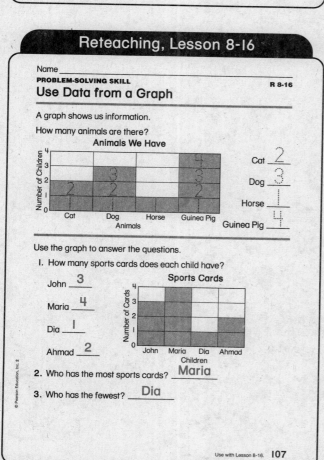

Animals We Have

Cat   2
Dog   3
Horse 1
Guinea Pig 4

Use the graph to answer the questions.

1. How many sports cards does each child have?

John 3

Maria 4

Dia   1

Ahmad 2

Sports Cards

2. Who has the most sports cards? Maria

3. Who has the fewest? Dia

Use with Lesson 8-16. **107**

Practice, Lesson 8-16

Name _____

PROBLEM-SOLVING SKILL

Use Data from a Graph

P 8-16

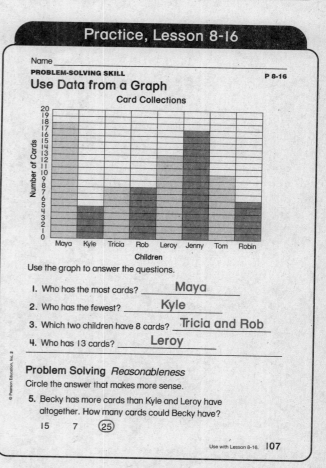

Card Collections

Use the graph to answer the questions.

1. Who has the most cards? Maya

2. Who has the fewest? Kyle

3. Which two children have 8 cards? Tricia and Rob

4. Who has 13 cards? Leroy

Problem Solving *Reasonableness*

Circle the answer that makes more sense.

5. Becky has more cards than Kyle and Leroy have altogether. How many cards could Becky have?

15   7   (25)

Use with Lesson 8-16. **107**

55

Name _____

PROBLEM-SOLVING APPLICATIONS   R 8-17

Fly, Butterfly, Fly!

The short hand tells the hour 1: _____.

The long hand tells the minutes _____:30.

The time is ___1:30___ .

Write the time.

1. The butterfly rests on a flower.

   ___11:00___

2. The butterfly leaves the flower.

   ___11:15___

3. How long did the butterfly stay on the flower?

   ___15 minutes___

Writing in Math

4. Write a sentence about what the butterfly did next. Tell how long it took and show the time on the clock.

___Answers will vary. Clock should reflect___

___elapsed time.___

Name _____

PROBLEM-SOLVING APPLICATIONS   P 8-17

Fly, Butterfly, Fly!

Solve.

1. A butterfly landed on a plant at 3:00. It stayed there for 10 minutes. Then it flew away.

   It flew away at ___3:10___ .

2. There are 17 butterflies in a garden. 8 more butterflies come to join them. How many butterflies are in the garden now?

   ___17___ + ___8___ = ___25___ butterflies

3. Linda has 23 butterflies in a collection. She gives away 6 butterflies. How many butterflies are in her collection now?

   ___23___ ⊖ ___6___ = ___17___ butterflies

Writing in Math

Write a story about a butterfly.

___Stories will vary.___

_____

_____

_____

Name _____

Understanding Length and Height

R 9-1

Height is how tall an object is.
You can use cubes to measure height.
Line up the cubes with the ends
of the object.

about __2__ cubes tall

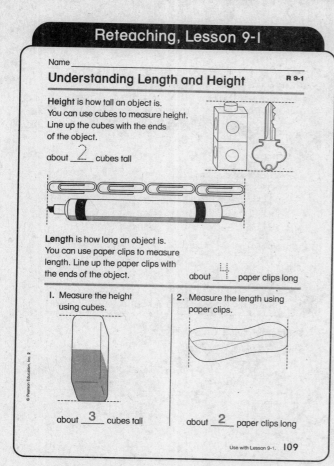

Length is how long an object is.
You can use paper clips to measure
length. Line up the paper clips with
the ends of the object.

about __4__ paper clips long

1. Measure the height using cubes.

about __3__ cubes tall

2. Measure the length using paper clips.

about __2__ paper clips long

Use with Lesson 9-1. 109

Name _____

Understanding Length and Height

P 9-1

Measure each classroom object using cubes or paper
clips. Circle the word or words that make sense.

Answers will vary.

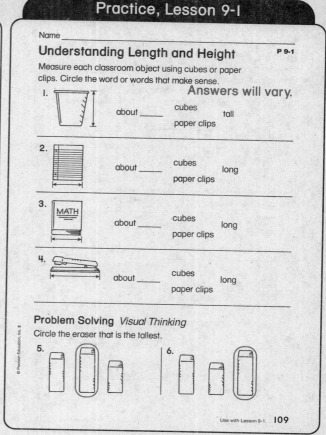

1. about _____ cubes / paper clips / tall

2. about _____ cubes / paper clips / long

3. about _____ cubes / paper clips / long

4. about _____ cubes / paper clips / long

Problem Solving *Visual Thinking*
Circle the eraser that is the tallest.

5.   6.

Use with Lesson 9-1. 109

Name _____

Inches and Feet

R 9-2

Use a ruler to measure inches or feet.

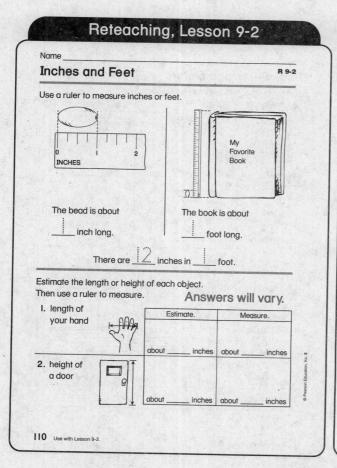

The bead is about
__1__ inch long.

The book is about
__1__ foot long.

There are __12__ inches in __1__ foot.

Estimate the length or height of each object.
Then use a ruler to measure.   **Answers will vary.**

1. length of your hand

	Estimate.	Measure.
	about _____ inches	about _____ inches

2. height of a door

| | about _____ inches | about _____ inches |

Name _____

Inches and Feet

P 9-2

Estimate the length or height of each object.
Then use a ruler to measure.

Answers will vary.

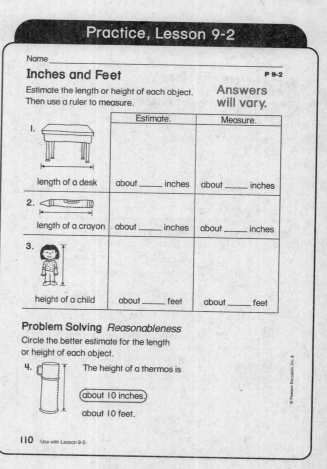

	Estimate.	Measure.
1. length of a desk	about _____ inches	about _____ inches
2. length of a crayon	about _____ inches	about _____ inches
3. height of a child	about _____ feet	about _____ feet

Problem Solving *Reasonableness*
Circle the better estimate for the length
or height of each object.

4. The height of a thermos is

(about 10 inches.)

about 10 feet.

Name _____

Inches, Feet, and Yards

R 9-3

Use inches to measure short lengths.
Use feet to measure medium-sized lengths.
Use **yards** to measure long lengths.

Remember:
3 feet = 1 yard
36 inches = 1 yard

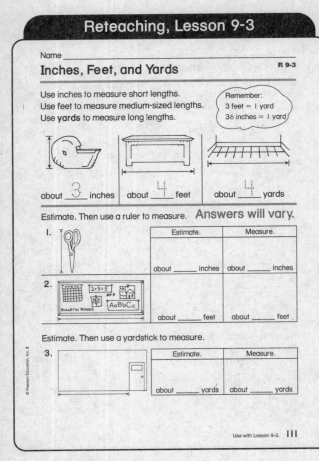

about __3__ inches   about __4__ feet   about __4__ yards

Estimate. Then use a ruler to measure. **Answers will vary.**

	Estimate.	Measure.
1.	about _____ inches	about _____ inches
2.	about _____ feet	about _____ feet

Estimate. Then use a yardstick to measure.

	Estimate.	Measure.
3.	about _____ yards	about _____ yards

© Pearson Education, Inc. 2

Use with Lesson 9-3.   111

Name _____

Inches, Feet, and Yards

P 9-3

Estimate the width, height, or length of each object.
Then use a ruler or a yardstick to measure.   **Answers will vary.**

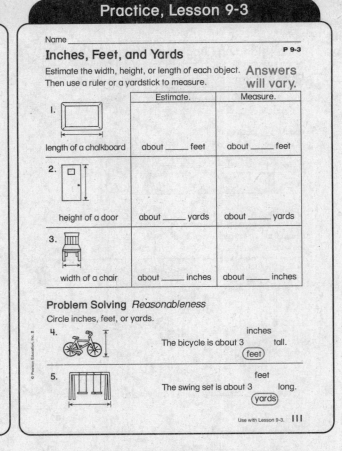

	Estimate.	Measure.
1. length of a chalkboard	about _____ feet	about _____ feet
2. height of a door	about _____ yards	about _____ yards
3. width of a chair	about _____ inches	about _____ inches

Problem Solving *Reasonableness*

Circle inches, feet, or yards.

4. The bicycle is about 3 __inches__ (feet) tall.

5. The swing set is about 3 __feet__ (yards) long.

© Pearson Education, Inc. 2

Use with Lesson 9-3.   111

Name _____

Centimeters and Meters

R 9-4

Centimeters are used to measure short lengths.
Meters are used to measure long lengths.

There are 100 centimeters in 1 meter.

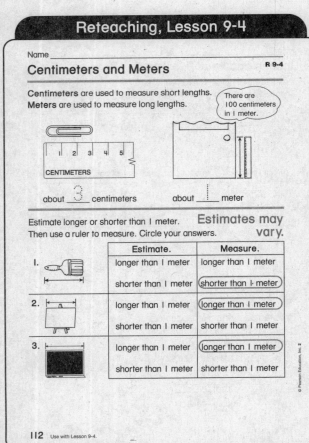

about __3__ centimeters   about __1__ meter

Estimate longer or shorter than 1 meter.   **Estimates may vary.**
Then use a ruler to measure. Circle your answers.

	Estimate.	Measure.
1.	longer than 1 meter / shorter than 1 meter	longer than 1 meter / (shorter than 1 meter)
2.	longer than 1 meter / shorter than 1 meter	(longer than 1 meter) / shorter than 1 meter
3.	longer than 1 meter / shorter than 1 meter	(longer than 1 meter) / shorter than 1 meter

© Pearson Education, Inc. 2

112 Use with Lesson 9-4.

Name _____

Centimeters and Meters

P 9-4

Estimate the length or height of each object.
Then use a ruler to measure.   **Answers will vary.**

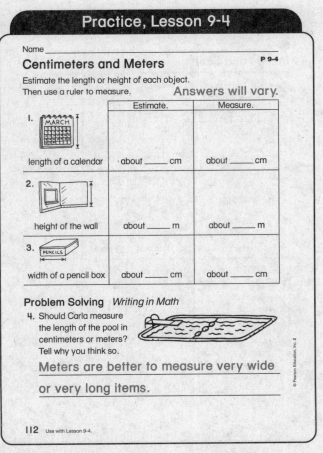

	Estimate.	Measure.
1. length of a calendar	about _____ cm	about _____ cm
2. height of the wall	about _____ m	about _____ m
3. width of a pencil box	about _____ cm	about _____ cm

Problem Solving *Writing in Math*

4. Should Carla measure
the length of the pool in
centimeters or meters?
Tell why you think so.

Meters are better to measure very wide
or very long items.

© Pearson Education, Inc. 2

112 Use with Lesson 9-4.

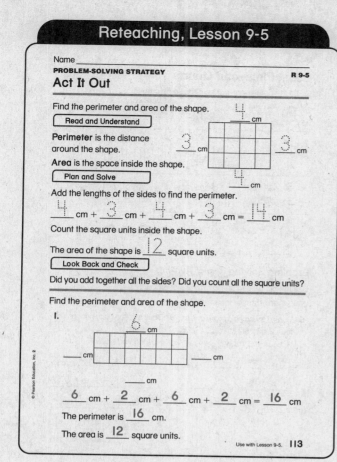

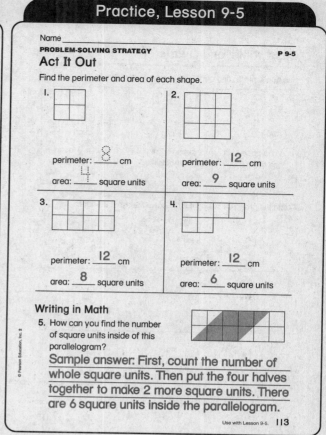

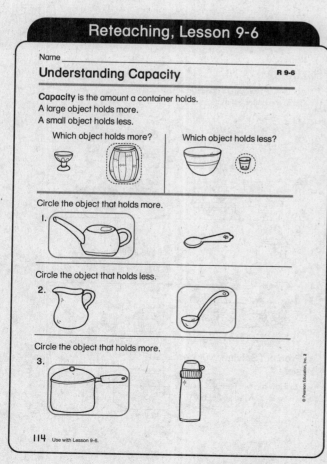

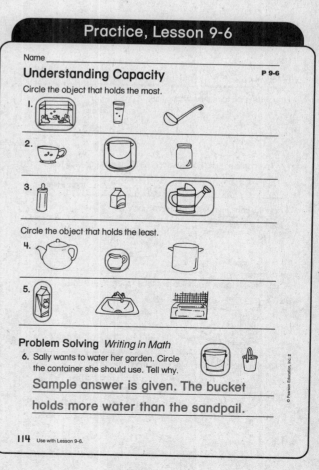

Reteaching, Lesson 9-5

Name _____

PROBLEM-SOLVING STRATEGY   R 9-5

Act It Out

Find the perimeter and area of the shape.

| Read and Understand |

Perimeter is the distance around the shape.

Area is the space inside the shape.

| Plan and Solve |

Add the lengths of the sides to find the perimeter.

__4__ cm + __3__ cm + __4__ cm + __3__ cm = __14__ cm

Count the square units inside the shape.

The area of the shape is __12__ square units.

| Look Back and Check |

Did you add together all the sides? Did you count all the square units?

Find the perimeter and area of the shape.

1.

__6__ cm + __2__ cm + __6__ cm + __2__ cm = __16__ cm

The perimeter is __16__ cm.

The area is __12__ square units.

Use with Lesson 9-5. 113

Practice, Lesson 9-5

Name _____

PROBLEM-SOLVING STRATEGY   P 9-5

Act It Out

Find the perimeter and area of each shape.

1.

perimeter: __8__ cm

area: __4__ square units

2.

perimeter: __12__ cm

area: __9__ square units

3.

perimeter: __12__ cm

area: __8__ square units

4.

perimeter: __12__ cm

area: __6__ square units

Writing in Math

5. How can you find the number of square units inside of this parallelogram?

Sample answer: First, count the number of whole square units. Then put the four halves together to make 2 more square units. There are 6 square units inside the parallelogram.

Use with Lesson 9-5. 113

Reteaching, Lesson 9-6

Name _____

Understanding Capacity   R 9-6

Capacity is the amount a container holds.
A large object holds more.
A small object holds less.

Which object holds more?

Which object holds less?

Circle the object that holds more.

1.

Circle the object that holds less.

2.

Circle the object that holds more.

3.

114 Use with Lesson 9-6.

Practice, Lesson 9-6

Name _____

Understanding Capacity   P 9-6

Circle the object that holds the most.

1.

2.

3.

Circle the object that holds the least.

4.

5.

Problem Solving *Writing in Math*

6. Sally wants to water her garden. Circle the container she should use. Tell why.

Sample answer is given. The bucket holds more water than the sandpail.

114 Use with Lesson 9-6.

59

Name _____

Cups, Pints, and Quarts

R 9-7

Use **cups**, **pints**, and **quarts** to measure capacity.

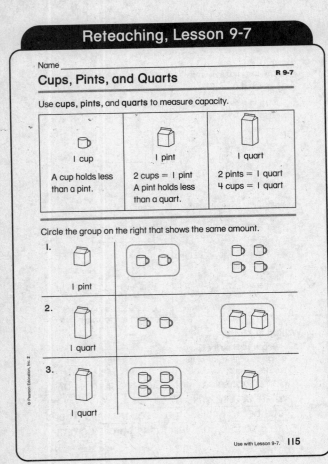

I cup	I pint	I quart
A cup holds less than a pint.	2 cups = I pint A pint holds less than a quart.	2 pints = I quart 4 cups = I quart

Circle the group on the right that shows the same amount.

1. I pint

2. I quart

3. I quart

© Pearson Education, Inc. 2

Name _____

Cups, Pints, and Quarts

P 9-7

Circle the containers that hold the same amount.

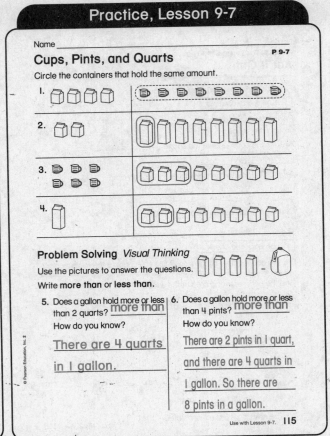

1.

2.

3.

4.

Problem Solving *Visual Thinking*

Use the pictures to answer the questions.
Write **more than** or **less than.**

5. Does a gallon hold more or less than 2 quarts? _more than_
   How do you know?

   There are 4 quarts in I gallon.

6. Does a gallon hold more or less than 4 pints? _more than_
   How do you know?

   There are 2 pints in I quart, and there are 4 quarts in I gallon. So there are 8 pints in a gallon.

© Pearson Education, Inc. 2

Name _____

Liters

R 9-8

Liters are used to measure capacity.

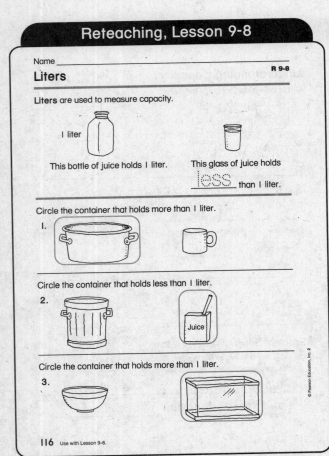

I liter

This bottle of juice holds I liter.

This glass of juice holds _less_ than I liter.

Circle the container that holds more than I liter.

1.

Circle the container that holds less than I liter.

2.   Juice

Circle the container that holds more than I liter.

3.

© Pearson Education, Inc. 2

Name _____

Liters

P 9-8

About how many liters does the object hold?
Circle the better estimate.

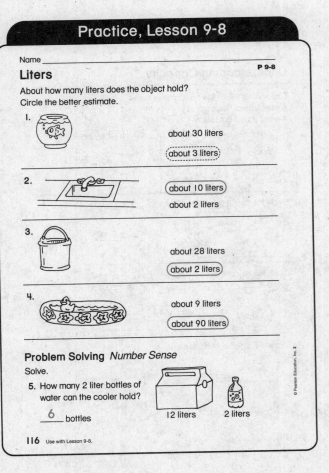

1. about 30 liters
   (about 3 liters)

2. (about 10 liters)
   about 2 liters

3. about 28 liters
   (about 2 liters)

4. about 9 liters
   (about 90 liters)

Problem Solving *Number Sense*

Solve.

5. How many 2 liter bottles of water can the cooler hold?

   __6__ bottles

   12 liters   2 liters

© Pearson Education, Inc. 2

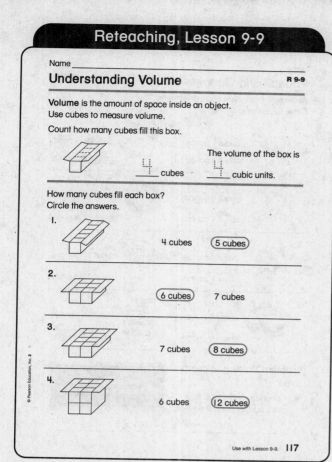

Name _____

Understanding Volume

R 9-9

Volume is the amount of space inside an object.
Use cubes to measure volume.

Count how many cubes fill this box.

__4__ cubes

The volume of the box is
__4__ cubic units.

How many cubes fill each box?
Circle the answers.

1. 4 cubes (5 cubes)

2. (6 cubes) 7 cubes

3. 7 cubes (8 cubes)

4. 6 cubes (12 cubes)

Use with Lesson 9-9. 117

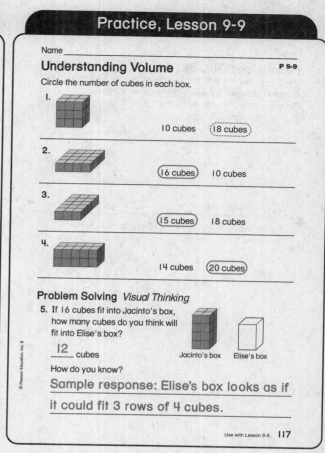

Name _____

Understanding Volume

P 9-9

Circle the number of cubes in each box.

1. 10 cubes (18 cubes)

2. (16 cubes) 10 cubes

3. (15 cubes) 18 cubes

4. 14 cubes (20 cubes)

Problem Solving *Visual Thinking*

5. If 16 cubes fit into Jacinto's box, how many cubes do you think will fit into Elise's box?

__12__ cubes

Jacinto's box   Elise's box

How do you know?

Sample response: Elise's box looks as if it could fit 3 rows of 4 cubes.

Use with Lesson 9-9. 117

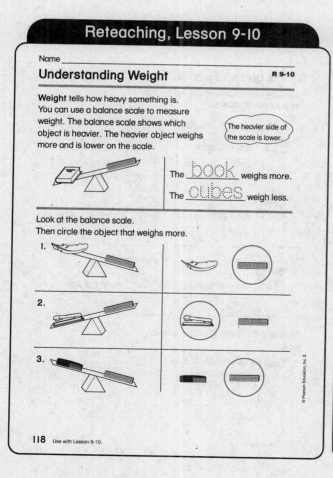

Name _____

Understanding Weight

R 9-10

Weight tells how heavy something is.
You can use a balance scale to measure weight. The balance scale shows which object is heavier. The heavier object weighs more and is lower on the scale.

The heavier side of the scale is lower.

The __book__ weighs more.
The __cubes__ weigh less.

Look at the balance scale.
Then circle the object that weighs more.

1.

2.

3.

118   Use with Lesson 9-10.

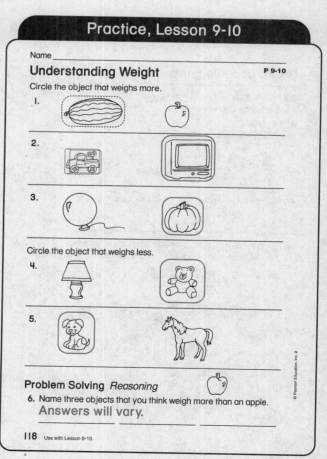

Name _____

Understanding Weight

P 9-10

Circle the object that weighs more.

1.

2.

3.

Circle the object that weighs less.

4.

5.

Problem Solving *Reasoning*

6. Name three objects that you think weigh more than an apple.
Answers will vary.

118   Use with Lesson 9-10.

Pounds and Ounces

R 9-11

Name _____

Ounces are used to measure light things.
Pounds are used to measure heavier things.

Remember:
1 pound = 16 ounces.

The book weighs about 1 pound.

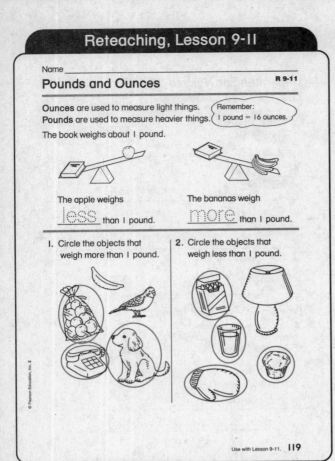

The apple weighs
less than 1 pound.

The bananas weigh
more than 1 pound.

1. Circle the objects that weigh more than 1 pound.

2. Circle the objects that weigh less than 1 pound.

Pounds and Ounces

P 9-11

Name _____

About how much does each object weigh?
Circle the better estimate.

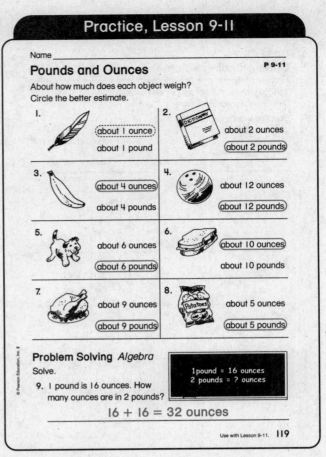

1. (about 1 ounce)
   about 1 pound

2. about 2 ounces
   (about 2 pounds)

3. (about 4 ounces)
   about 4 pounds

4. about 12 ounces
   (about 12 pounds)

5. about 6 ounces
   (about 6 pounds)

6. (about 10 ounces)
   about 10 pounds

7. about 9 ounces
   (about 9 pounds)

8. about 5 ounces
   (about 5 pounds)

Problem Solving *Algebra*

Solve.

1 pound = 16 ounces
2 pounds = ? ounces

9. 1 pound is 16 ounces. How many ounces are in 2 pounds?

16 + 16 = 32 ounces

Grams and Kilograms

R 9-12

Name _____

Grams are used to measure light things.
Kilograms are used to measure heavier things.

Remember:
1,000 grams = 1 kilogram.

The shoe measures about 1 kilogram.

The balloon measures
less than 1 kilogram.

The clock measures
more than 1 kilogram.

1. Circle the objects that measure more than 1 kilogram.

2. Circle the objects that measure less than 1 kilogram.

Grams and Kilograms

P 9-12

Name _____

About how much does each object measure?
Circle the better estimate.

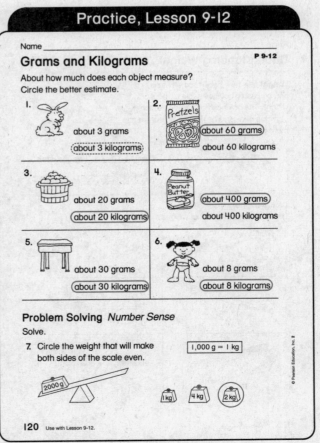

1. about 3 grams
   (about 3 kilograms)

2. (about 60 grams)
   about 60 kilograms

3. about 20 grams
   (about 20 kilograms)

4. (about 400 grams)
   about 400 kilograms

5. about 30 grams
   (about 30 kilograms)

6. about 8 grams
   (about 8 kilograms)

Problem Solving *Number Sense*

Solve.

1,000 g = 1 kg

7. Circle the weight that will make both sides of the scale even.

2000 g

1 kg   4 kg   (2 kg)

Name _____

Temperature: Fahrenheit and Celsius

R 9-13

Temperature tells how hot or how cold.
You can measure temperature in **Fahrenheit.**

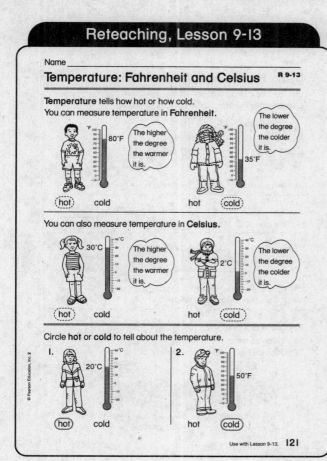

You can also measure temperature in **Celsius.**

Circle **hot** or **cold** to tell about the temperature.

1.   20°C   (hot)   cold

2.   50°F   hot   (cold)

Use with Lesson 9-13. **121**

Name _____

Temperature: Fahrenheit and Celsius

P 9-13

Color to show the temperature.
Circle **hot** or **cold** to tell about the temperature.

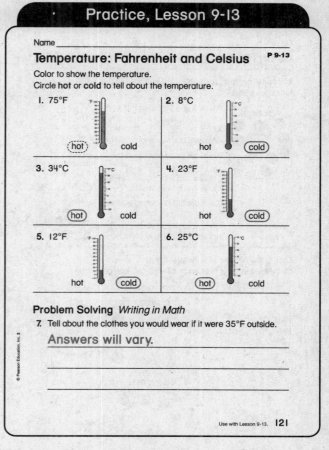

1. 75°F   (hot)   cold

2. 8°C   hot   (cold)

3. 34°C   (hot)   cold

4. 23°F   hot   (cold)

5. 12°F   hot   (cold)

6. 25°C   (hot)   cold

Problem Solving *Writing in Math*

7. Tell about the clothes you would wear if it were 35°F outside.

Answers will vary.
_____
_____

Use with Lesson 9-13. **121**

Name _____

Understanding Probability

R 9-14

Probability is when you predict if something
is **more likely** or **less likely** to happen.

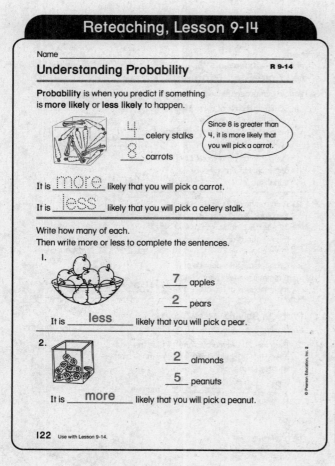

$\frac{4}{8}$ celery stalks
carrots

Since 8 is greater than 4, it is more likely that you will pick a carrot.

It is more likely that you will pick a carrot.

It is less likely that you will pick a celery stalk.

Write how many of each.
Then write more or less to complete the sentences.

1.
    7 apples
    2 pears

It is less likely that you will pick a pear.

2.
    2 almonds
    5 peanuts

It is more likely that you will pick a peanut.

122 Use with Lesson 9-14.

Name _____

Understanding Probability

P 9-14

If you were to spin once, which color is
the spinner most likely to land on?

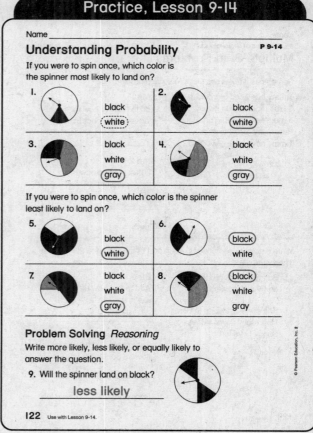

1.   black   (white)

2.   black   (white)

3.   black   white   (gray)

4.   black   white   (gray)

If you were to spin once, which color is the spinner
least likely to land on?

5.   black   (white)

6.   (black)   white

7.   black   white   (gray)

8.   (black)   white   gray

Problem Solving *Reasoning*

Write more likely, less likely, or equally likely to
answer the question.

9. Will the spinner land on black?

less likely

122 Use with Lesson 9-14.

63

Name _____

R 9-15

Using Probability

Words like **certain**, **probable**, and **impossible**
tell about probability.

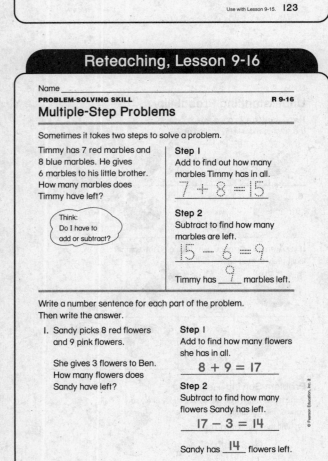

You pick one button from the jar.

It is *certain* that you
will pick a black or a gray button.

> **Certain** means it will happen.

There are more black buttons.

It is *probable* that
you will pick a black button.

> **Probable** means it is most likely to happen.

There are not any white buttons.

It is *impossible*
that you will pick a white button.

> **Impossible** means that it will <u>not</u> happen.

Look at the number of buttons in the jar.
Circle the button or buttons that tell about each probability.

You pick one button from the jar.

1. It is **certain** that you will pick

2. It is **probable** that you will pick

3. It is **impossible** that you will pick

Use with Lesson 9-15. **123**

Name _____

P 9-15

Using Probability

Use the tally chart to help you answer the questions.
Circle the missing word to complete the sentence.

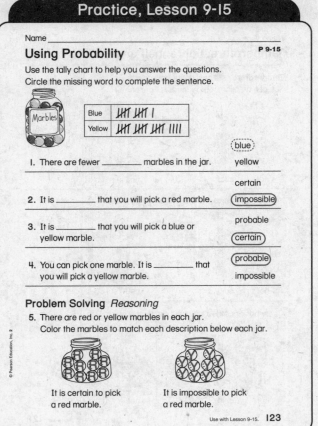

| Blue | JHT JHT I |
| Yellow | JHT JHT JHT IIII |

1. There are fewer _____ marbles in the jar.
   (blue) yellow

2. It is _____ that you will pick a red marble.
   certain (impossible)

3. It is _____ that you will pick a blue or
   yellow marble.
   probable (certain)

4. You can pick one marble. It is _____ that
   you will pick a yellow marble.
   (probable) impossible

Problem Solving *Reasoning*

5. There are red or yellow marbles in each jar.
   Color the marbles to match each description below each jar.

It is certain to pick
a red marble.

It is impossible to pick
a red marble.

Use with Lesson 9-15. **123**

Name _____

PROBLEM-SOLVING SKILL

R 9-16

Multiple-Step Problems

Sometimes it takes two steps to solve a problem.

Timmy has 7 red marbles and
8 blue marbles. He gives
6 marbles to his little brother.
How many marbles does
Timmy have left?

> Think:
> Do I have to
> add or subtract?

Step 1
Add to find out how many
marbles Timmy has in all.

$7 + 8 = 15$

Step 2
Subtract to find how many
marbles are left.

$15 - 6 = 9$

Timmy has _9_ marbles left.

Write a number sentence for each part of the problem.
Then write the answer.

1. Sandy picks 8 red flowers
   and 9 pink flowers.

   She gives 3 flowers to Ben.
   How many flowers does
   Sandy have left?

   Step 1
   Add to find how many flowers
   she has in all.

   $8 + 9 = 17$

   Step 2
   Subtract to find how many
   flowers Sandy has left.

   $17 - 3 = 14$

   Sandy has _14_ flowers left.

124 Use with Lesson 9-16.

Name _____

PROBLEM-SOLVING SKILL

P 9-16

Multiple-Step Problems

Write a number sentence for each part of the problem.

1. Sam puts 8 cups of apple juice
   and 9 cups of grape juice in a
   party punch. How many cups are
   in the punch?

   $8 + 9 = 17$ cups

   People at the party drink 11 cups
   of punch. How many cups of
   punch are left?

   $17 - 11 = 6$ cups

2. A basket holds 21 pounds of
   tomatoes. Another basket holds
   14 pounds of tomatoes. How
   many pounds of tomatoes are
   there altogether?

   $21 + 14 = 35$ pounds

   Grandpa uses 16 pounds of
   tomatoes to make sauce. How
   many pounds of tomatoes are left?

   $35 - 16 = 19$ pounds

Problem Solving *Mental Math*

Solve using mental math.

3. Beth has 20 red marbles and 15 blue marbles.
   Joyce has 40 yellow marbles. How many marbles
   do they have in all?

   $20 + 15 + 40 = 75$ marbles

124 Use with Lesson 9-16.

© Pearson Education, Inc. 2

Name _____

PROBLEM-SOLVING APPLICATIONS　　　　　　　　　R 9-17

How Do You Measure Up?

You can use pounds to measure how
heavy or how light something is.

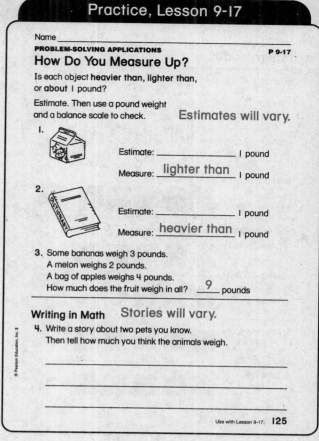

The box of blocks
weighs more than
the book.

The book
weighs about
1 pound.

The eraser
weighs less
than the book.

The box of blocks is _____ 1 pound.　　less than　　（more than）

The eraser is _____ 1 pound.　　（less than）　　more than

Is it more or less than 1 pound?
Circle your estimate. Then measure.

Answers will vary.

	Estimate.	Measure.
1. (soccer ball)	less than	less than
	more than	more than
2. (headphones)	less than	less than
	more than	more than

Writing in Math

3. Choose an object in your classroom.
   Estimate and measure how much it weighs.
   Write about what you find.

   Answers will vary.

   _____

Name _____

PROBLEM-SOLVING APPLICATIONS　　　　　　　　　P 9-17

How Do You Measure Up?

Is each object **heavier than, lighter than,**
or **about** 1 pound?

Estimate. Then use a pound weight
and a balance scale to check.　　**Estimates will vary.**

1. (box)

   Estimate: _____ 1 pound

   Measure: lighter than 1 pound

2. (book)

   Estimate: _____ 1 pound

   Measure: heavier than 1 pound

3. Some bananas weigh 3 pounds.
   A melon weighs 2 pounds.
   A bag of apples weighs 4 pounds.
   How much does the fruit weigh in all?　____9____ pounds

Writing in Math　Stories will vary.

4. Write a story about two pets you know.
   Then tell how much you think the animals weigh.

   _____

   _____

   _____

Name _____

Building 1,000

R 10-1

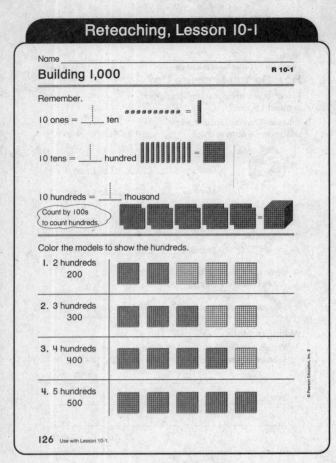

Remember.

10 ones = __1__ ten   ◾◾◾◾◾◾◾◾◾◾ = ▮

10 tens = __1__ hundred   ▮▮▮▮▮▮▮▮▮▮ = ◼

10 hundreds = _____ thousand

(Count by 100s to count hundreds.)

◼ ◼ ◼ ◼ ◼ ◼ = 🔲

Color the models to show the hundreds.

1. 2 hundreds
   200

2. 3 hundreds
   300

3. 4 hundreds
   400

4. 5 hundreds
   500

126 Use with Lesson 10-1.

© Pearson Education, Inc. 2

Name _____

Building 1,000

P 10-1

Write how many. Use models if you need to.

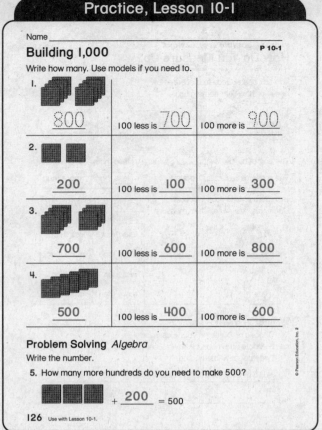

1. __800__   100 less is __700__   100 more is __900__

2. __200__   100 less is __100__   100 more is __300__

3. __700__   100 less is __600__   100 more is __800__

4. __500__   100 less is __400__   100 more is __600__

Problem Solving *Algebra*

Write the number.

5. How many more hundreds do you need to make 500?

◼ ◼ ◼ + __200__ = 500

126 Use with Lesson 10-1.

© Pearson Education, Inc. 2

Name _____

Counting Hundreds, Tens, and Ones

R 10-2

You can write a 3-digit number counting hundreds, tens, and ones.

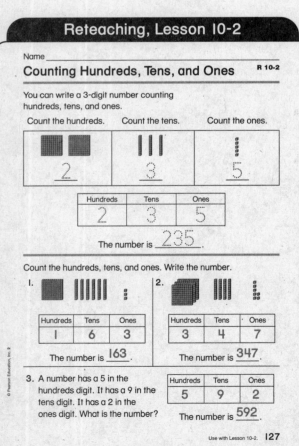

Count the hundreds.   Count the tens.   Count the ones.

__2__   __3__   __5__

Hundreds	Tens	Ones
2	3	5

The number is __235__.

Count the hundreds, tens, and ones. Write the number.

1.
Hundreds	Tens	Ones
1	6	3

The number is __163__.

2.
Hundreds	Tens	Ones
3	4	7

The number is __347__.

3. A number has a 5 in the hundreds digit. It has a 9 in the tens digit. It has a 2 in the ones digit. What is the number?

Hundreds	Tens	Ones
5	9	2

The number is __592__.

Use with Lesson 10-2. **127**

© Pearson Education, Inc. 2

Name _____

Counting Hundreds, Tens, and Ones

P 10-2

Write the numbers.
Use models and Workmat 5 if you need to.

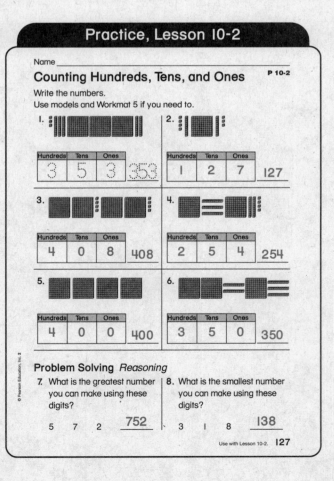

1.
Hundreds	Tens	Ones	
3	5	3	353

2.
Hundreds	Tens	Ones	
1	2	7	127

3.
Hundreds	Tens	Ones	
4	0	8	408

4.
Hundreds	Tens	Ones	
2	5	4	254

5.
Hundreds	Tens	Ones	
4	0	0	400

6.
Hundreds	Tens	Ones	
3	5	0	350

Problem Solving *Reasoning*

7. What is the greatest number you can make using these digits?

5 7 2   __752__

8. What is the smallest number you can make using these digits?

3 1 8   __138__

Use with Lesson 10-2. **127**

© Pearson Education, Inc. 2

66

Name _____

Writing Numbers to 1,000

R 10-3

Expanded form uses plus signs to show hundreds, tens, and ones.

$200 + 60 + 4$

You can draw models to show expanded form.

The **number word** is two hundred sixty-four.

The **standard form** is

264

Draw models to show the expanded form.
Write the number in standard form.

1. $400 + 30 + 8$ four hundred thirty-eight

438

2. $300 + 70 + 2$ three hundred seventy-two

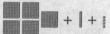

372

3. $500 + 10 + 4$ five hundred fourteen

514

Name _____

Writing Numbers to 1,000

P 10-3

Circle the models to match the expanded form.
Write the number in standard form.

1. $200 + 70 + 5$ 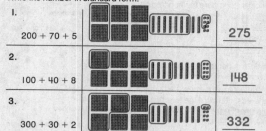   275

2. $100 + 40 + 8$ 148

3. $300 + 30 + 2$ 332

Circle the models to match the standard form.
Write the number in expanded form.

4. 571   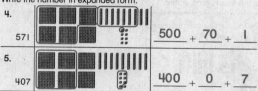 $500 + 70 + 1$

5. 407 $400 + 0 + 7$

Problem Solving *Mental Math*

Write the total.

6. Crayons come in boxes of 10. How many boxes do you need for 100 crayons? ___10___ boxes

10 crayons = 1 box

Name _____

Changing Numbers by Hundreds and Tens

R 10-4

When you change a number by adding or subtracting tens, only the tens digit changes.

$100 + 30 + 6 = 136$

(Think: 10 more)

$136 + 10 = \underline{146}$

(Think: 20 less)

$136 - 20 = \underline{116}$

When you change a number by adding or subtracting hundreds, only the hundreds digit changes.

$300 + 50 + 3 = 353$

(Think: 100 more)

$353 + 100 = \underline{453}$

(Think: 200 less)

$353 - 200 = \underline{153}$

Underline the digits that change. Then solve the problem.

1.

$4\underline{4}6 + 20 = \underline{466}$

$\underline{4}46 + 200 = \underline{646}$

$400 + 40 + 6 = 446$

2.

$5\underline{3}8 - 30 = \underline{508}$

$\underline{5}38 - 300 = \underline{238}$

$500 + 30 + 8 = 538$

Name _____

Changing Numbers by Hundreds and Tens

P 10-4

Use models, drawings, or mental math to solve the problem.

1. $362 - 10 = \underline{352}$

$362 - 100 = \underline{262}$

2. $148 + 40 = \underline{188}$

$148 + 400 = \underline{548}$

3. $594 - 30 = \underline{564}$

$594 - 300 = \underline{294}$

4. $433 + 20 = \underline{453}$

$433 + 200 = \underline{633}$

Problem Solving *Number Sense*

Solve.

5. Mickey has 234 baseball cards. He gets 50 more cards. How many cards does he have now?

___284___ cards

6. Dixie has 426 baseball cards. She gives away 200 cards. How many cards does she have now?

___226___ cards

Reteaching, Lesson 10-5

Name _____

Comparing Numbers

R 10-5

To compare two numbers with unequal hundreds, compare the hundreds first.

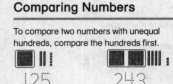

125   243

Remember:
$<$ is less than

Think: 1 hundred is less than 2 hundreds. So, 125 $<$ 243.

To compare two numbers with equal hundreds, compare the tens first.

243   217

Remember:
$>$ is greater than

Think: 4 tens is greater than 1 ten. So, 243 $>$ 217.

Write the number in standard form.
Then compare. Write $>$ or $<$.

1.

455    $>$ 326

2.

313    $<$ 323

130 Use with Lesson 10-5.

© Pearson Education, Inc. 2

Practice, Lesson 10-5

Name _____

Comparing Numbers

P 10-5

Compare. Write $>$, $<$, or $=$. Use models if you need to.

1. 157 $<$ 214   361 $<$ 378   419 $<$ 516

2. 600 $>$ 598   771 $=$ 771   645 $>$ 546

3. 197 $<$ 217   505 $<$ 550   987 $>$ 978

4. 384 $<$ 478   727 $>$ 582   408 $<$ 804

Problem Solving *Visual Thinking*

5. Draw lines to match the clues with the correct model.

My number is less than 5 hundreds. The ones digit is less than 7.

My number is greater than 3 hundreds. The tens digit is greater than 5.

My number has more than 3 hundreds. There are 0 tens in the number.

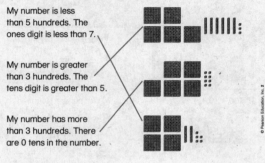

130 Use with Lesson 10-5.

© Pearson Education, Inc. 2

Reteaching, Lesson 10-6

Name _____

Parts of 1,000

R 10-6

There are different ways to make 1,000.
You can count on by 100s and by 10s to make 1,000.

Start with 650.   Count on by 100s.   Count on by 10s.

100 200 300   10 20 30 40 50
750, 850, 950   960, 970, 980, 990, 1,000

650 + 300 + 50 = 1,000

650 + 350 = 1,000

Find the parts for 1,000.
Count on by 100s. Then count on by 10s.

1. Start with 750.

100 200   10 20 30 40 50

750 + 200 + 50 = 1,000

750 + 250 = 1,000

2. Start with 500.

100 200 300 400 500

500 + 500 = 1,000

Use with Lesson 10-6. 131

© Pearson Education, Inc. 2

Practice, Lesson 10-6

Name _____

Parts of 1,000

P 10-6

Count on to solve each problem.

1. Kayla has 850 points. How many more points does she need to get to 1,000?

   850 + 150 = 1,000

   150 points

2. Abdul has 550 points. If he needs 1,000 points to win, how many more points does he need?

   550 + 450 = 1,000

   450 points

3. Monty has 700 points. He needs 1,000 points to win. How many more points does he need?

   700 + 300 = 1,000

   300 points

4. Suki has 350 points. How many more points does she need to get to 1,000?

   350 + 650 = 1,000

   650 points

Problem Solving *Number Sense*

Find the missing number.

5. Misha has 250 points. Tasia has 300 points. They need 1,000 points to win. How many more points do they need?

   250 + 300 + __?__ = 1,000   450 points

Use with Lesson 10-6. 131

© Pearson Education, Inc. 2

Name _____

PROBLEM-SOLVING SKILL   R 10-7

Use Data from a Chart

You can use a chart to solve
problems. This chart shows
the points scored on a video game.

Points Scored	
Dan	356
Naomi	617
Philip	582
Lucy	298

Who scored more points,
Dan or Naomi?

Look at the chart for the points
that Dan and Naomi scored.

Dan scored __356__ points.

Naomi scored __617__ points.

356 ⊙ 617 __Naomi__ scored more points.

Use the chart to answer the questions.

1. Who scored more points, Philip or Lucy?

   Philip scored __582__ points. 582 ⊙ 298

   Lucy scored __298__ points. __Philip__ scored more points.

2. Who scored more points, Lucy or Naomi?

   Lucy scored __298__ points. 298 ⊙ 617

   Naomi scored __617__ points. __Naomi__ scored more points.

3. Who scored 300 + 50 + 6 points? __Dan__

132 Use with Lesson 10-7.

Name _____

PROBLEM-SOLVING SKILL   P 10-7

Use Data from a Chart

Use data from the chart to
answer the questions.

Number of People at the Games	
Basketball	465
Baseball	390
Soccer	288
Hockey	432

1. Did more people come to
   the baseball game or the
   hockey game? __the hockey game__

2. Which game did
   400 + 60 + 5 people
   come to watch? __the basketball game__

3. 2 hundreds, 8 tens, and
   8 ones tells how many people
   came to which game? __the soccer game__

Problem Solving *Reasonableness*
Circle the number that makes the most sense.

4. About 50 / ⟨500⟩ people are watching basketball.

5. About ⟨300⟩ / 30 people are watching soccer.

Circle the words that make more sense.

6. The number of people at a basketball game is
   the number of people at a hockey game. less than / ⟨greater than⟩

132 Use with Lesson 10-7.

Name _____

Before, After, and Between   R 10-8

Think about the order of numbers.

| 150 | 151 | 152 | 153 | 154 | 155 | 156 | 157 | 158 | 159 |
| 160 | 161 | 162 | 163 | 164 | 165 | 166 | 167 | 168 | 169 |

__152__ is **before** 153. __168__ is **after** 167.

__161__ is **between** 160 and 162.

Write the numbers that are before, after, and between.

1.

| 300 | 301 | 302 | 303 | 304 | 305 | 306 | 307 | 308 | 309 |
| 310 | 311 | 312 | 313 | 314 | 315 | 316 | 317 | 318 | 319 |

__313__ is **before** 314. __305__ is **after** 304.

__304__ is **between** 303 and 305.

2.

| 750 | 751 | 752 | 753 | 754 | 755 | 756 | 757 | 758 | 759 |
| 760 | 761 | 762 | 763 | 764 | 765 | 766 | 767 | 768 | 769 |

__764__ is **before** 765. __759__ is **after** 758.

__753__ is **between** 752 and 754.

3.

| 530 | 531 | 532 | 533 | 534 | 535 | 536 | 537 | 538 | 539 |
| 540 | 541 | 542 | 543 | 544 | 545 | 546 | 547 | 548 | 549 |

__548__ is **before** 549. __531__ is **after** 530.

__542__ is **between** 541 and 543.

Use with Lesson 10-8. **133**

Name _____

Before, After, and Between   P 10-8

Write the number that comes after.

1. 235, __236__   489, __490__   600, __601__

2. 319, __320__   899, __900__   534, __535__

Write the number that comes before.

3. __729__, 730   __404__, 405   __336__, 337

4. __799__, 800   __178__, 179   __297__, 298

Write the number that comes between.

5. 375, __376__, 377   819, __820__, 821   197, __198__, 199

6. 199, __200__, 201   450, __451__, 452   834, __835__, 836

Write the number.

7. What is one before 278? __277__

8. What is one after 743? __744__

9. What number is between 681 and 683? __682__

Problem Solving *Reasoning*
Circle the numbers.

10. Which two numbers come after 297?   213 ⟨307⟩ ⟨299⟩

11. Which two numbers come before 810?   ⟨775⟩ ⟨801⟩ 811

12. Which two numbers come between 400   ⟨425⟩ 465 ⟨419⟩
    and 450?

Use with Lesson 10-8. **133**

Name _____

Ordering Numbers

R 10-9

These numbers are in order from least to greatest.

167 < 270 < 273 < 499

Each number is less than (<) the number after it.

These numbers are in order from greatest to least.

684 > 680 > 371 > 262

Each number is greater than (>) the number after it.

Order the numbers from least to greatest.

275 543 110 212

110 < 212 < 275 < 543

Order the numbers from greatest to least.

616 583 775 102

775 > 616 > 583 > 102

Write the numbers in order from least to greatest.

1. 187 126 219 267   126, 187, 219, 267

2. 341 489 452 317   317, 341, 452, 489

Write the numbers in order from greatest to least.

3. 419 578 535 487   578, 535, 487, 419

4. 682 734 546 650   734, 682, 650, 546

© Pearson Education, Inc. 2

Name _____

Ordering Numbers

P 10-9

Write the numbers in order from least to greatest.

1. 673, 628, 515, 437, 321

321, 437, 515, 628, 673

2. 423, 409, 457, 524, 582

409, 423, 457, 524, 582

3. 507, 387, 652, 481, 658

387, 481, 507, 652, 658

4. 198, 277, 156, 287, 192

156, 192, 198, 277, 287

Write the numbers in order from greatest to least.

5. 731, 682, 432, 819, 688

819, 731, 688, 682, 432

6. 331, 287, 207, 432, 211

432, 331, 287, 211, 207

Problem Solving *Writing in Math*

Use the space on the right to solve the problems.

7. In the numbers 572 to 592, are there more even or odd numbers? How do you know?

There are more even numbers. There are 10 odd numbers and 11 even numbers.

© Pearson Education, Inc. 2

Name _____

PROBLEM-SOLVING STRATEGY

Look for a Pattern

R 10-10

A pattern is something that repeats.

Read and Understand

Look for a pattern rule to find what number comes next.
What number comes next? 280, 270, 260, 250, 240, __?__

Plan and Solve

Think. What digit changes?   280, 270, 260, 250, 240   10s

Think. Does it increase or decrease?   280, 270, 260, 250, 240   decrease

Think. By how much?   280, 270, 260, 250, 240   by 10

The pattern rule is The numbers decrease by 10.

The next number is 230 .

Look Back and Check

Does your answer fit the pattern rule?

Write the numbers that come next. Describe the pattern rule.

1. 285, 385, 485, 585, 685, 785, 885, 985

The pattern rule is: The numbers increase by 100.

2. 340, 360, 380, 400, 420, 440, 460, 480

The pattern rule is: The numbers increase by 20.

© Pearson Education, Inc. 2

Name _____

PROBLEM-SOLVING STRATEGY

Look for a Pattern

P 10-10

Write the missing numbers. Describe the pattern.

1. 185, 195, 205, 215, 225, 235, 245

The numbers increase by 10, or the tens digits increase by 1.

Write the number that is 50 less.

2. 778   690   187   958

   728   640   137   908

What pattern do you see? The tens digits decrease by 5.

Write the number that is 300 more.

3. 205   537   169   649

   505   837   469   949

What pattern do you see? The hundreds digits increase by 3.

Problem Solving *Reasoning*

Find the pattern. Circle the number that comes next.

4. 105, 125, 145, 165   166   (185)   175

5. 300, 325, 350, 375   500   476   (400)

6. 550, 600, 650, 700   725   (750)   800

© Pearson Education, Inc. 2

Name _____

PROBLEM-SOLVING APPLICATIONS   R 10-11
Rescue Vehicles

Fire truck A has 600 gallons of water. Fire truck B has 100 more gallons.

Fire truck A: ■■■■■■

Fire truck B: ■■■■■■+■

$600 + 100 = 700$

100 more than 600 is

__700__ gallons.

Fire truck C has 500 gallons of water. It uses 100 gallons to put out a fire.

Fire truck C: ■■■■■

Gallons used: ■■■■✖

$500 - 100 = 400$

100 less than 500 is

__400__ gallons.

Solve.

1. A firefighter goes on 30 calls in one month. How much is 10 calls less than that?

$30 - 10 =$ __20__ calls

How much is 10 calls more than that?

$30 + 10 =$ __40__ calls

2. A fire truck travels 400 miles in one month. How much is 100 miles more than that?   __500__ miles

How much is 100 miles less than that?   __300__ miles

136 Use with Lesson 10-11.

© Pearson Education, Inc. 2

Name _____

PROBLEM-SOLVING APPLICATIONS   P 10-11
Rescue Vehicles

1. A fire truck traveled 267 miles in one month to put out fires. Record the number of hundreds, tens, and ones in 267.

__2__ hundreds   __6__ tens   __7__ ones

2. A fire boat had 215 calls in one year. It had 198 calls the next year. Compare these two numbers. Write >, <, or =.

215 ⊘ 198

3. A fire truck responded to an alarm at quarter past 10. What is another way to write this time?

__10:15__

Writing in Math

4. Write a number story about an ambulance. Use four numbers between 200 and 300. At the end of your story, list the numbers in order from greatest to least.

Check children's math.

_____

_____

_____

136 Use with Lesson 10-11.

© Pearson Education, Inc. 2

71

Using Mental Math

Name _____

Add 315 + 264. Use mental math.

To add using mental math, begin with the expanded form of each number. Then add each place value.

315 →   300 + 10 + 5   500 + 70 + 9 = 579
264 → + 200 + 60 + 4
      500 + 70 + 9   So, 315 + 264 = 579

Add.

1. 523 + 172 = ___?___

523 → 500 + 20 + 3
172 → + 100 + 70 + 2
     600 + 90 + 5

600 + 90 + 5 = 695

So, 523 + 172 = 695

2. 281 + 716 = ___?___

281 → 200 + 80 + 1
716 → + 700 + 10 + 6
     900 + 90 + 7

900 + 90 + 7 = 997

So, 281 + 716 = 997

3. 193 + 605 = ___?___

193 → 100 + 90 + 3
605 → + 600 + 0 + 5
     700 + 90 + 8

700 + 90 + 8 = 798

So, 193 + 605 = 798

Using Mental Math

Name _____

Add. Use mental math.

1. 306 + 213 = __519__   515 + 262 = __777__

2. 164 + 311 = __475__   623 + 123 = __746__

3. 412 + 250 = __662__   322 + 146 = __468__

4. __707__ = 303 + 404   711 + 105 = __816__

5. 271 + 320 = __591__   __439__ = 319 + 120

6. 409 + 230 = __639__   725 + 114 = __839__

Problem Solving *Algebra*

Write the missing number that makes the number sentence true.

7. 400 + 500 = 600 + __300__   8. 200 + __700__ = 700 + 200

9. 300 + 200 = 0 + __500__   10. 500 + 400 = 900 + __0__

11. 100 + 700 = 400 + __400__   12. 600 + __300__ = 800 + 100

Estimating Sums

Name _____

You can estimate to find an answer that is close to the exact sum. To estimate, find the closest hundred.

Estimate 185 + 437. Is it more than or less than 500?

Is 185 closer to 100 or 200? 200

Is 437 closer to 400 or 500? 400

200 + 400 = 600

So, 185 + 437 is more than 500.

Is the sum more or less than the number?
Estimate the sum. Write **more than** or **less than**.

1. Is 179 + 267 more than or less than 600?

179 is close to 200.   267 is close to 300.

200 + 300 = 500.

179 + 267 is less than 600.

2. Is 327 + 417 more than or less than 600?

327 is close to 300.   417 is close to 400.

300 + 400 = 700.

327 + 417 is more than 600.

Estimating Sums

Name _____

Is the sum more or less than the number?
Estimate the sum. Then write **more than** or **less than**.

1. Is 283 + 250 more than or less than 500?   __more than__ 500

2. Is 415 + 403 more than or less than 850?   __less than__ 850

3. Is 367 + 298 more than or less than 650?   __more than__ 650

4. Is 454 + 432 more than or less than 900?   __less than__ 900

5. Is 277 + 519 more than or less than 750?   __more than__ 750

Problem Solving *Number Sense*

Look at the cards. Choose a number that will make each sentence true.

6. 382 + __224__ is about 600.

7. 378 + __101__ is less than 600.

8. 211 + __440__ is more than 600.

224   440   101

Name _____

Adding with Models

R 11-3

135 + 248 = _____

Step 1: Add the ones. Regroup if you need to.
Step 2: Add the tens. Regroup if you need to.
Step 3: Add the hundreds.

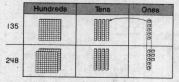

	Hundreds	Tens	Ones
135			
248			

5 + 8 = 13 ones.
Regroup 10 ones
for 1 ten.

135 + 248 = 383

Add to find the sum. Use models and Workmat 5.
Show each number.

1.

Hundreds	Tens	Ones

341 + 127 = 468

2.

Hundreds	Tens	Ones

524 + 249 = 773

Use with Lesson 11-3. **139**

Name _____

Adding with Models

P 11-3

Use models and Workmat 5. Show each number.
Add to find the sum.

1. 407 + 188 = 595	2. 182 + 253 = 435
3. 270 + 319 = 589	4. 685 = 558 + 127
5. 376 + 508 = 884	6. 427 = 194 + 233

Problem Solving *Estimation*

Circle the best estimate.

7.

Grade	Number of Children
1	235
2	189

About how many children
are in both grades?

300 (400) 500

8.

Grade	Number of Children
3	429
4	311

About how many children
are in both grades?

600 (700) 800

9. Each floor of the school holds
145 children. About how many
children can the school hold
if there are 2 floors?

150   250   (300)

Use with Lesson 11-3. **139**

Name _____

Adding Three-Digit Numbers

R 11-4

Step 1: Add the ones. Regroup if you need to.
Step 2: Add the tens. Regroup if you need to.
Step 3: Add the hundreds.

Think:
Regroup 10 tens
for 1 hundred.

163 + 174 = ?

Hundreds	Tens	Ones
1	6	3
+ 1	7	4
3	3	7

Draw to regroup. Add.

1. 218 + 136 = ?

Hundreds	Tens	Ones
2	1	8
+ 1	3	6
3	5	4

Add. Use models and Workmat 5 if you need to.

2.

Hundreds	Tens	Ones
1	2	5
+ 2	4	2
3	6	7

3.

Hundreds	Tens	Ones
4	1	9
+ 2	5	6
6	7	5

140 Use with Lesson 11-4.

Name _____

Adding Three-Digit Numbers

P 11-4

Add. Use models and Workmat 5 if you need to.

1.

Hundreds	Tens	Ones
	1	
6	3	4
+ 1	5	9
7	9	3

Hundreds	Tens	Ones
1		
1	2	9
+ 4	9	0
6	1	9

2.

457	219	405	286	124
+ 138	+ 390	+ 263	+ 491	+ 209
595	609	668	777	333

Problem Solving *Number Sense*

3. For the problems, use each number for only one digit.

3 5 6 2 4 1

Make the greatest sum.   Make the least sum.

2	7	2
+ 6	5	4
9	2	6

2	7	2
+ 1	2	3
3	9	5

140 Use with Lesson 11-4.

© Pearson Education, Inc. 2

73

Name _____

Practice with Three-Digit Addition

R 11-5

417 + 163 = ?

Rewrite the problem using the workmat.

Line up the hundreds, tens, and ones.
1. Add the ones. Regroup if you need to.
2. Add the tens. Regroup if you need to.
3. Add the hundreds.

Hundreds	Tens	Ones
□	1	
4	1	7
+ 1	6	3
5	8	0

Write the addition problem. Find the sum.

1. 152 + 341

Hundreds	Tens	Ones
□		
1	5	2
+ 3	4	1
4	9	3

374 + 183

Hundreds	Tens	Ones
1		
3	7	4
+ 1	8	3
5	5	7

560 + 278

Hundreds	Tens	Ones
1		
5	6	0
+ 2	7	8
8	3	8

2. 415 + 142

Hundreds	Tens	Ones
□		
4	1	5
+ 1	4	2
5	5	7

192 + 173

Hundreds	Tens	Ones
1		
1	9	2
+ 1	7	3
3	6	5

307 + 378

Hundreds	Tens	Ones
1		
3	0	7
+ 3	7	8
6	8	5

Use with Lesson 11-5. 141

Name _____

Practice with Three-Digit Addition

P 11-5

Write the addition problem. Find the sum.

1.
$$291 + 105 \quad \begin{array}{r} 291 \\ +105 \\ \hline 396 \end{array}$$
$$315 + 482 \quad \begin{array}{r} 315 \\ +482 \\ \hline 797 \end{array}$$
$$158 + 771 \quad \begin{array}{r} 1 \\ 158 \\ +771 \\ \hline 929 \end{array}$$

2.
$$463 + 142 \quad \begin{array}{r} 1 \\ 463 \\ +142 \\ \hline 605 \end{array}$$
$$37 + 517 \quad \begin{array}{r} 1 \\ 37 \\ +517 \\ \hline 554 \end{array}$$
$$428 + 149 \quad \begin{array}{r} 1 \\ 428 \\ +149 \\ \hline 577 \end{array}$$

3.
$$219 + 168 \quad \begin{array}{r} 1 \\ 219 \\ +168 \\ \hline 387 \end{array}$$
$$537 + 92 \quad \begin{array}{r} 1 \\ 537 \\ +92 \\ \hline 629 \end{array}$$
$$502 + 238 \quad \begin{array}{r} 1 \\ 502 \\ +238 \\ \hline 740 \end{array}$$

Problem Solving *Number Sense*

Solve the number riddles.

4. When I am added to 210, the sum is 864. What number am I? __654__

5. When I am added to 103, the sum is 333. What number am I? __230__

Use with Lesson 11-5. 141

Name _____

PROBLEM-SOLVING STRATEGY   R 11-6

Make a Graph

How many second graders ride the bus?

200 second graders from Willow Town ride the bus.
250 second graders from Dandy Creek ride the bus.

Read and Understand

Find out how many second graders in all ride the bus.

Plan and Solve

First, add the number of second graders from both towns.

200
+ 250
‾‾‾‾
450

450 second graders ride the bus.

Then, add this information to the graph.

Look Back and Check

Does the bar above second graders stop at 450?

Children Riding the Bus

Read the problems. Add to find how many in all.
Then complete the graph.

1. 150 first graders from Willow Town ride the bus. 200 first graders from Dandy Creek ride the bus.

__350__ first graders in all.

2. 350 third graders from Willow Town ride the bus. 250 third graders from Dandy Creek ride the bus.

__600__ third graders in all.

142 Use with Lesson 11-6.

Name _____

PROBLEM-SOLVING STRATEGY   P 11-6

Make a Graph

Use the chart to answer the questions.

Art Supplies			
	Crayons	Paints	Brushes
Art Room 1	350	200	300
Art Room 2	400	150	250

1. How many crayons are there in all?

__750__ crayons

2. How many paints are there in all? __350__ paints

3. How many brushes are there in all? __550__ brushes

4. Use your answers from Exercises 1–3 to complete the graph. Color to show how many of each of the art supplies there are in all.

Art Supplies

Problem Solving *Writing in Math*

Answers may vary. Possible response given.

5. How is a bar graph different from a chart?

A bar graph uses bars to show numbers.

142 Use with Lesson 11-6.

Name _____

Ways to Find Missing Parts

R 11-7

Count on by hundreds and tens to find the parts of the whole.

260 + _____ = 700

First, count on by hundreds.   4 hundreds

260, $\overset{\frown}{360}$ $\overset{\frown}{460}$ $\overset{\frown}{560}$ $\overset{\frown}{660}$
    100   200   300   400

Next, count on by tens.   4 tens

660, $\overset{\frown}{670}$ $\overset{\frown}{680}$ $\overset{\frown}{690}$ $\overset{\frown}{700}$
   10   20   30   40

4 hundreds and 4 tens is 440.

700	
260	440

So, 260 + **440** = 700

I. 350 + __?__ = 600

Count on by hundreds.   **2** hundreds

350, **450**, **550**

Count on by tens.   **5** tens

550, **560**, **570**, **580**, **590**, **600**

2 hundreds and **5** tens is **250**.

So, 350 + **250** = 600

© Pearson Education, Inc. 2

Name _____

Ways to Find Missing Parts

P 11-7

Count on or count back to find the missing part.

1. 360 + **240** = 600
2. 420 + **280** = 700
3. 180 + **520** = 700
4. 500 = 170 + **330**
5. 270 + **630** = 900
6. 420 + **180** = 600
7. 700 = 390 + **310**
8. 500 = **360** + 140

Problem Solving *Algebra*

Circle the weights you would need to balance each scale.

9.

10.

11.

© Pearson Education, Inc. 2

Name _____

Estimating Differences

R 11-8

You can estimate to find an answer that is close to the exact difference. To estimate, find the closest hundred.

Estimate 596 − 221.

Is 596 closer to 500 or 600?   **600**

Is 221 closer to 200 or 300?   **200**

600 − **200** = **400**

So, 596 − 221 is about **400**.

Circle the estimate that best matches each problem.

I. 502 − 105	is about	200	300	(400)
2. 909 − 403	is about	(500)	600	700
3. 615 − 412	is about	100	(200)	300
4. 511 − 298	is about	(200)	300	400
5. 881 − 500	is about	300	(400)	500
6. 231 − 108	is about	(100)	200	300
7. 799 − 182	is about	400	500	(600)
8. 627 − 275	is about	200	(300)	400

© Pearson Education, Inc. 2

Name _____

Estimating Differences

P 11-8

Circle the problem that matches the estimate.

I. about 400	718 − 487	or	(921 − 513)
2. about 200	933 − 567	or	(478 − 301)
3. about 100	(684 − 572)	or	376 − 123
4. about 500	(834 − 311)	or	769 − 487
5. about 300	659 − 147	or	(801 − 490)
6. about 600	714 − 588	or	(899 − 312)

Problem Solving *Number Sense*

For the problems, choose a set of 3 numbers.
Use each number one time. Subtract to solve.

2 5 7   1   4 6

7. Make the greatest difference.   8. Make the least difference.

  9 5 0
− **1** **2** **4**
  8 2 6

  9 5 0
− **7** **6** **5**
  1 **8** 5

© Pearson Education, Inc. 2

Name _____

Subtracting with Models

R 11-9

327 − 164 = ___?___

Step 1: Subtract the ones. Regroup if you need to.
Step 2: Subtract the tens. Regroup if you need to.
Step 3: Subtract the hundreds.

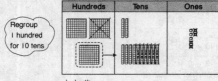

Regroup 1 hundred for 10 tens

Hundreds	Tens	Ones

327 − 164 = _163_

Subtract to find the difference. Use models and Workmat 5.
Show each number.

1.

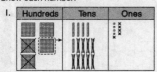

Hundreds	Tens	Ones

549 − 295 = _254_

2.

Hundreds	Tens	Ones

835 − 516 = _319_

Use with Lesson 11-9. **145**

Name _____

Subtracting with Models

P 11-9

Subtract. Use models and Workmat 5.

1. 476 − 321 = _155_	2. 659 − 372 = _287_
3. 953 − 209 = _744_	4. _119_ = 561 − 442
5. 390 − 126 = _264_	6. 732 − 121 = _611_
7. _286_ = 578 − 292	8. 818 − 409 = _409_

Problem Solving *Reasoning*

9. Write the name of each child below
the cards he or she collects.

Sports Card Collection

- Jake has about 300 more cards than Cindi.
- Melba has the most cards.
- William has about 100 less cards than Melba.

600 cards	200 cards	705 cards	510 cards
William	Cindi	Melba	Jake

Use with Lesson 11-9. **145**

Name _____

Subtracting Three-Digit Numbers

R 11-10

Step 1: Subtract the ones. Regroup if you need to.
Step 2: Subtract the tens. Regroup if you need to.
Step 3: Subtract the hundreds.

Think: Regroup 1 ten for 10 ones.

362 − 125 = ___?___

Hundreds	Tens	Ones

	Hundreds	Tens	Ones
	3	5 6	2 12
−	1	2	5
	2	3	7

Draw to regroup. Subtract.

1. 429 − 174 = ___?___

Hundreds	Tens	Ones

	Hundreds	Tens	Ones
	3	12	
	4	2	9
−	1	7	4
	2	5	5

Subtract. Use models and Workmat 5 if you need to.

2.

Hundreds	Tens	Ones
5	7	4
− 2	1	3
3	6	1

3.

Hundreds	Tens	Ones
	7	18
7	8	8
− 2	6	9
5	1	9

146 Use with Lesson 11-10.

Name _____

Subtracting Three-Digit Numbers

P 11-10

Subtract. Use models and Workmat 5 if you need to.

1.

Hundreds	Tens	Ones
7	8	4
− 2	5	1
5	3	3

Hundreds	Tens	Ones
	7	15
4	8	5
− 1	3	9
3	4	6

2.

Hundreds	Tens	Ones
4	17	
5	7	8
− 2	9	7
2	8	1

Hundreds	Tens	Ones
5	12	
6	2	4
− 3	3	2
2	9	2

3.

417	416	710	614	
657	561	809	742	927
− 128	− 390	− 263	− 450	− 304
529	171	546	292	623

Problem Solving *Visual Thinking*

Circle the weight you need to remove to balance the scale.

4.

350   150   225   125

146 Use with Lesson 11-10.

© Pearson Education, Inc. 2

76

Name _____

Practice with Three-Digit Subtraction   R 11-11

528 − 143 = __?__

Rewrite the problem using the workmat.

Line up the hundreds, tens, and ones.
Subtract the ones. Regroup if you need to.
Subtract the tens. Regroup if you need to.
Subtract the hundreds.

Hundreds	Tens	Ones
4	12	
5̶	2̶	8
1	4	3
3	8	5

Write the subtraction problem. Find the difference.

1.

648 − 217

Hundreds	Tens	Ones
6	4	8
2	1	7
4	3	1

593 − 264

Hundreds	Tens	Ones
	8	13
5	9̶	3̶
2	6	4
3	2	9

435 − 192

Hundreds	Tens	Ones
3	13	
4̶	3̶	5
1	9	2
2	4	3

2.

328 − 114

Hundreds	Tens	Ones
3	2	8
1	1	4
2	1	4

782 − 329

Hundreds	Tens	Ones
	7	12
7	8̶	2̶
3	2	9
4	5	3

957 − 173

Hundreds	Tens	Ones
8	15	
9̶	5̶	7
1	7	3
7	8	4

Use with Lesson 11-11. 147

Name _____

Practice with Three-Digit Subtraction   P 11-11

Write the subtraction problem. Find the difference.

1.
```
  639
 -218
  421
```
```
  512
  56̶2
 -129
  433
```
```
  814
  94̶7
 -351
  596
```

2.
```
  711
  8̶1̶7
 -253
  564
```
```
  610
  70̶7
 - 95
  612
```
```
  478
 -321
  157
```

3.
```
  418
  5̶8̶9
 -193
  396
```
```
  313
  64̶3
 -228
  415
```
```
  410
  85̶0
 - 49
  801
```

Problem Solving *Estimation*

Circle the best estimate.

4. 624 − 410   100 (200) 300

5. 934 − 411   (500) 600 700

6. 776 − 187   400 500 (600)

Use with Lesson 11-11. 147

Name _____

PROBLEM-SOLVING SKILL   R 11-12

Exact Answer or Estimate

James collects 321 cans for recycling day. He needs 550 cans to win a prize. How many more cans does James need?

Subtract to find the **exact** amount of cans James needs.

```
  550
 -321
  229
```

__229__ cans

Genie collects 387 cans. Sandra collects 134 cans. About how many more cans does Genie collect than Sandra?

To find out **about** how many more cans, use an estimate.

387 is about 400
134 is about 100
```
  400
 -100
  300
```

about __300__ more

Circle **estimate** or **exact answer**. Solve.

1. Aleesha collects 327 newspapers. She needs 650 to fill a carton. How many more papers does she need?

(exact answer) estimate

Subtract to find the answer.

```
   4 10
  6 5̶ 0̶
 -3 2 7
  3 2 3
```
__323__ more

2. Nan collects 167 plastic bottles. She collects 219 glass bottles. About how many bottles does she collect in all?

exact answer (estimate)

Add to find the answer.

```
  200
 +200
```
about __400__ bottles

148 Use with Lesson 11-12.

Name _____

PROBLEM-SOLVING SKILL   P 11-12

Exact Answer or Estimate

Circle **estimate** or **exact answer**.
Answer the question.

1. A train travels 312 miles on Monday and 478 miles on Tuesday. About how many miles did the train travel on both days?

(estimate) exact answer

Sample estimate is given.
```
  300
 +500
  800
```

__about 800 miles__

2. There are 517 children at the Elm Street school. 325 children take the bus to school. How many children do not take the bus to school?

estimate (exact answer)

```
  411
  5̶1̶7
 -325
  192
```

__192 children__

3. Mrs. Cook reads a book with 572 pages. She has read about 300 pages. About how many pages does she have left to read?

(estimate) exact answer

Sample estimate is given.
```
  600
 -300
  300
```

__about 300 pages__

Problem Solving *Writing in Math*

4. Write a math problem in which an exact answer is needed.

__Problems will vary.__

148 Use with Lesson 11-12.

77

Name _____

PROBLEM-SOLVING APPLICATIONS R 11-13

Amazing Animals

You can add to solve problems with three-digit numbers.

A tree frog lays 134 eggs. Another tree frog lays 182 eggs. How many eggs did they lay in all?

Add to find how many in all.

```
  1 3 4
+ 1 8 2
-------
  3 1 6  eggs
```

You can subtract to solve problems with three-digit numbers.

A male lion weighs 475 pounds. A female lion weighs 384 pounds. How many more pounds does the male weigh?

Subtract to find how many more.

```
  3 1 7
  4 7 5
- 3 8 4
-------
    9 1  more pounds
```

Solve.

1. A rain forest tree is 238 feet tall. Another tree is 172 feet tall. How much taller is the first tree?

   Subtract to find the answer.

   __66__ feet taller

   ```
   [1][13][ ]
    2  3  8
   - 1  7  2
   --------
      6  6
   ```

2. A group of tourists travels 387 miles to a rain forest. Then they travel 152 miles through the rain forest. How many miles did they travel in all?

   Add to find the answer.

   __539__ miles

   ```
      1
    3 8 7
  + 1 5 2
  -------
    5 3 9
   ```

Name _____

PROBLEM-SOLVING APPLICATIONS P 11-13

Amazing Animals

Solve.

1. A monkey sits on a tree that is 115 feet high. The monkey climbs 60 feet. Then it climbs another 50 feet. How high is the monkey now?

   __225__ feet

2. One week, a group of chimpanzees ate 500 bananas. The next week, they ate 300 bananas. How many more bananas did the chimpanzees eat in the first week?

   __200__ more bananas

3. A toucan sits on a branch that is 212 feet high. Another toucan sits on a branch that is 108 feet high. How much higher is the first toucan?

   __104__ feet higher

Writing in Math

4. Write a subtraction story about your favorite rain forest animal. Use three-digit numbers in your story.

   Stories will vary. _____

   _____

   _____

Name _____

Skip Counting Equal Groups

R 12-1

You can skip count **equal groups**
to find how many there are in all.

3 equal groups

2 birds in
each equal group

6 birds in all

1 equal group 2   1 equal group 4   1 equal group 6

Circle the equal groups.
Skip count to find out how many there are in all.

1.

1 equal group   1 equal group   1 equal group   1 equal group

4 equal groups

3 flowers in
each equal group

12 flowers in all

2.

3 equal groups

3 apples in
each equal group

9 apples in all

3.

2 equal groups

5 bananas in
each equal group

10 bananas in all

150 Use with Lesson 12-1.

© Pearson Education, Inc. 2

Name _____

Skip Counting Equal Groups

P 12-1

Draw to show equal groups. Skip count to find how
many there are in all. Use counters if you need to.

1. 2 groups, 5 in each group	2. 5 groups, 3 in each group
○○○○○ ○○○○○	Children should show 5 groups of 3 objects.
10 in all	15 in all
3. 4 groups, 2 in each group	4. 3 groups, 2 in each group
Children should show 4 groups of 2 objects.	Children should show 3 groups of 2 objects.
8 in all	6 in all

Problem Solving *Writing in Math*

Describe the skip counting pattern you use to find how many in all.

5.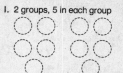

skip count by threes

6.

skip count by fives

150 Use with Lesson 12-1.

© Pearson Education, Inc. 2

Name _____

Repeated Addition and Multiplication

R 12-2

You can write an addition sentence
to tell how many there are in all.
You can write a multiplication sentence
to tell how many there are in all.

4 equal groups

2 in each group

$2 + 2 + 2 + 2 = 8$ in all

$4 \times 2 = 8$ in all

Write the number of equal groups.
Write how many there are in each group. Then write
an addition sentence and a multiplication sentence.

1.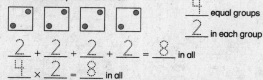

5 equal groups

3 in each group

$3 + 3 + 3 + 3 + 3 = 15$ in all

$5 \times 3 = 15$ in all

2.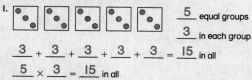

4 equal groups

4 in each group

$4 + 4 + 4 + 4 = 16$ in all

$4 \times 4 = 16$ in all

Use with Lesson 12-2. **151**

© Pearson Education, Inc. 2

Name _____

Repeated Addition and Multiplication

P 12-2

Write an addition sentence and a multiplication
sentence that tell how many there are in all.

1.

$3 + 3 + 3 = 9$ $3 \times 3 = 9$

2.

$2 + 2 + 2 + 2 = 8$ $4 \times 2 = 8$

3.

$4 + 4 + 4 + 4 + 4 = 20$ $5 \times 4 = 20$

4.

$6 + 6 + 6 = 18$ $3 \times 6 = 18$

5.

$6 + 6 = 12$ $2 \times 6 = 12$

Problem Solving *Number Sense*

6. Find the sum. Write a multiplication sentence
that shows the same amount.

$5 + 5 + 5 + 5 + 5 + 5 = 30$ $6 \times 5 = 30$

Use with Lesson 12-2. **151**

© Pearson Education, Inc. 2

79

Building Arrays

Name _____

A collection of objects arranged in equal rows and columns is an **array**. You can use an **array** to show equal groups.

Array

Circle each row. Count the number of rows.

There are __4__ rows.

Count the number of dots in each row.

There are __3__ dots in each row.

Write the multiplication sentence.

__4__ × __3__ = __12__ in all

Circle each row. Count the number of rows.
Count the number of dots in each row.
Write the multiplication sentence.

1.

There are __3__ rows.

There are __5__ dots in each row.

__3__ × __5__ = __15__ in all.

2.

There are __5__ rows.

There are __5__ dots in each row.

__5__ × __5__ = __25__ in all.

Building Arrays

Name _____

Write a multiplication sentence to describe each array.

1.

__3__ × __4__ = __12__

rows · in each row · in all

2.

__5__ × __2__ = __10__

3.

__4__ × __4__ = __16__

4.

__1__ × __5__ = __5__

5.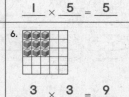

__3__ × __5__ = __15__

6.

__3__ × __3__ = __9__

Problem Solving *Visual Thinking*

7. Write the multiplication sentence for the shaded squares.

__4__ × __5__ = __20__

Multiplying in Any Order

Name _____

You can multiply numbers in any order and get the same product.

Color 3 rows with 2 in each row.

__3__ × __2__ = __6__

rows · in each row · in all

Color 2 rows with 3 in each row.

__2__ × __3__ = __6__

rows · in each row · in all

So, __3__ × __2__ is the same as __2__ × __3__.

Color the rows. Write the numbers.
Multiply to find the product.

1. Color 5 rows with 3 in each row.

__5__ × __3__ = __15__

rows · in each row · in all

Color 3 rows with 5 in each row.

__3__ × __5__ = __15__

rows · in each row · in all

So, __5__ × __3__ is the same as __3__ × __5__.

Multiplying in Any Order

Name _____

Write the numbers. Multiply to find the product.

1. __2__ rows

__4__ in each row

__2__ × __4__ = __8__

__4__ rows

__2__ in each row

__4__ × __2__ = __8__

2. __2__ rows

__5__ in each row

__2__ × __5__ = __10__

__5__ rows

__2__ in each row

__5__ × __2__ = __10__

Problem Solving *Algebra*

Complete the number sentences.

3.

3 × __5__ = 15

5 × __5__ = 25

Name _____

Vertical Form

R 12-5

You can write multiplication facts in two ways.

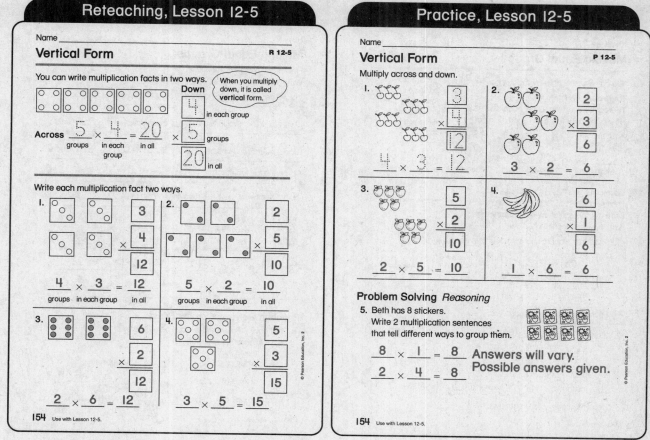

Down When you multiply down, it is called **vertical** form.

Across $\underline{5}$ × $\underline{4}$ = $\underline{20}$
groups   in each group   in all

4 in each group
× 5 groups
20 in all

Write each multiplication fact two ways.

1. [dominoes] × 3 / 4 / 12

$\underline{4}$ × $\underline{3}$ = $\underline{12}$
groups in each group in all

2. [dominoes] × 2 / 5 / 10

$\underline{5}$ × $\underline{2}$ = $\underline{10}$
groups in each group in all

3. [dominoes] × 6 / 2 / 12

$\underline{2}$ × $\underline{6}$ = $\underline{12}$

4. [dominoes] × 5 / 3 / 15

$\underline{3}$ × $\underline{5}$ = $\underline{15}$

154 Use with Lesson 12-5.

© Pearson Education, Inc. 2

Name _____

Vertical Form

P 12-5

Multiply across and down.

1. [cherries] × 3 / 4 / 12

$\underline{4}$ × $\underline{3}$ = $\underline{12}$

2. [apples] × 2 / 3 / 6

$\underline{3}$ × $\underline{2}$ = $\underline{6}$

3. [apples] × 5 / 2 / 10

$\underline{2}$ × $\underline{5}$ = $\underline{10}$

4. [bananas] × 6 / 1 / 6

$\underline{1}$ × $\underline{6}$ = $\underline{6}$

Problem Solving *Reasoning*

5. Beth has 8 stickers.
   Write 2 multiplication sentences
   that tell different ways to group them.

   $\underline{8}$ × $\underline{1}$ = $\underline{8}$ **Answers will vary.**
   $\underline{2}$ × $\underline{4}$ = $\underline{8}$ **Possible answers given.**

154 Use with Lesson 12-5.

© Pearson Education, Inc. 2

Name _____

PROBLEM-SOLVING STRATEGY

Draw a Picture

R 12-6

You can draw a picture to solve a problem.

[Read and Understand]

Francis knits 4 mittens. Each mitten has 5 buttons.
How many buttons are there in all?

What does the problem ask you to do?

Find how many buttons in all.

[Plan and Solve]

There are 4 mittens. Draw 5 buttons on each mitten.

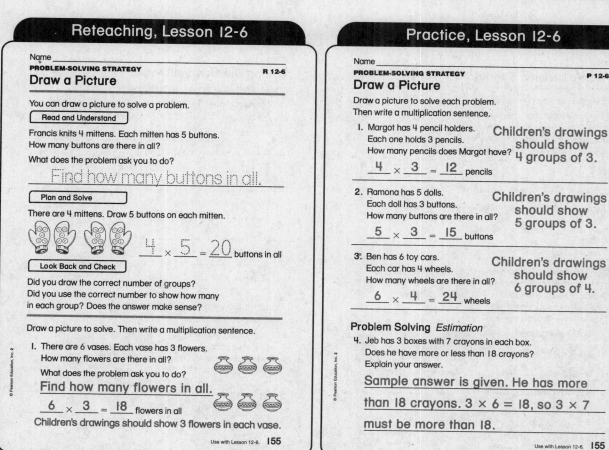

$\underline{4}$ × $\underline{5}$ = $\underline{20}$ buttons in all

[Look Back and Check]

Did you draw the correct number of groups?
Did you use the correct number to show how many
in each group? Does the answer make sense?

Draw a picture to solve. Then write a multiplication sentence.

1. There are 6 vases. Each vase has 3 flowers.
   How many flowers are there in all?

   What does the problem ask you to do?

   Find how many flowers in all.

   $\underline{6}$ × $\underline{3}$ = $\underline{18}$ flowers in all
   Children's drawings should show 3 flowers in each vase.

Use with Lesson 12-6. 155

© Pearson Education, Inc. 2

Name _____

PROBLEM-SOLVING STRATEGY

Draw a Picture

P 12-6

Draw a picture to solve each problem.
Then write a multiplication sentence.

1. Margot has 4 pencil holders.
   Each one holds 3 pencils.
   How many pencils does Margot have?   **Children's drawings should show 4 groups of 3.**

   $\underline{4}$ × $\underline{3}$ = $\underline{12}$ pencils

2. Ramona has 5 dolls.
   Each doll has 3 buttons.
   How many buttons are there in all?   **Children's drawings should show 5 groups of 3.**

   $\underline{5}$ × $\underline{3}$ = $\underline{15}$ buttons

3. Ben has 6 toy cars.
   Each car has 4 wheels.
   How many wheels are there in all?   **Children's drawings should show 6 groups of 4.**

   $\underline{6}$ × $\underline{4}$ = $\underline{24}$ wheels

Problem Solving *Estimation*

4. Jeb has 3 boxes with 7 crayons in each box.
   Does he have more or less than 18 crayons?
   Explain your answer.

   Sample answer is given. He has more

   than 18 crayons. 3 × 6 = 18, so 3 × 7

   must be more than 18.

Use with Lesson 12-6. 155

© Pearson Education, Inc. 2

Name _____

Making Equal Groups

R 12-7

You can share equally by making equal groups.

There are 9 counters in all.

There are 3 children. Draw equal shares.

How many counters does each child get?

> To make an **equal share**, give each child the same amount.

| Matthew | Aliki | Hannah |

Each child gets __3__ counters.

___

Draw counters to show equal shares.
Write how many each child gets.

I. 4 children want to share 16 counters equally.

| Philip | Elizabeth | Beto | Helen |

Each child gets __4__ counters.

___

2. 3 children want to share 15 counters equally.

| Sabrina | Moesha | Kyle |

Each child gets __5__ counters.

156 Use with Lesson 12-7.

© Pearson Education, Inc. 2

Name _____

Making Equal Groups

P 12-7

How many coins will each child get?
Write the answer. Use coins if you need to.

1. 15 pennies, 5 children   Each child gets __3__ pennies.

2. 20 nickels, 4 children   Each child gets __5__ nickels.

3. 12 quarters, 3 children   Each child gets __4__ quarters.

Complete the table.

	Number of coins	Number of children	How many coins does each child get?
4.	16	2	8
5.	9	3	3
6.	16	4	4
7.	14	7	2

Problem Solving *Number Sense*

8. You have 18 plums. Can you find 6 different ways to show equal groups?

__1__ group of __18__   __6__ groups of __3__

__2__ groups of __9__   __9__ groups of __2__

__3__ groups of __6__   __18__ groups of __1__

156 Use with Lesson 12-7.

© Pearson Education, Inc. 2

Name _____

Writing Division Sentences

R 12-8

When you share equally, you **divide**.

5 children want to share 10 counters equally. Draw 1 counter for each child. Keep drawing 1 counter for each child until you have drawn 10 counters in all.

| Brandon | Melissa | Joaquin | Dorothea | Janet |

There are __10__ counters to share equally.

There are __5__ groups of counters.

There are __2__ counters in each group.

Each child gets __2__ counters.   So, $10 \div 5 = 2$.

___

Draw to show equal groups.
Write how many each child gets.
Then write the division sentence.

I. 4 children want to share 12 counters.

| Gabriel | Talia | Shane | Natanya |

Each child gets __3__ counters. $12 \div 4 = 3$

© Pearson Education, Inc. 2

Use with Lesson 12-8. **157**

Name _____

Writing Division Sentences

P 12-8

Draw to show equal groups. Write the division sentence.

1. 9 markers divided among 3 boxes.

Children's drawings should show 3 groups with 3 markers in each.

$9 \div 3 = 3$

2. 12 buttons divided among 4 cups.

Children's drawings should show 4 groups with 3 buttons in each.

$12 \div 4 = 3$

3. 15 flowers divided among 5 vases.

Children's drawings should show 5 groups with 3 flowers in each.

$15 \div 5 = 3$

4. 8 balls divided among 2 cartons.

Children's drawings should show 2 groups with 4 balls in each.

$8 \div 2 = 4$

Problem Solving *Reasonableness*

Draw a picture to help answer the question.

5. Rita has 14 cat treats.
She has 3 cats.
How many treats will each cat get?
Are there any treats left over?

Children's drawings should show 3 groups of 4 cat treats, with 2 left over.

Each cat will get 4 treats and there will be 2 treats left over.

Use with Lesson 12-8. **157**

© Pearson Education, Inc. 2

Name _____

PROBLEM-SOLVING SKILL   R 12-9
Choose an Operation

Different operations solve different problems.
Write the sign that shows the operation you will
use to solve the problem; $+$, $-$, $\times$, or $\div$.

There are 5 cages at the pet store. 4 puppies are in
each cage. How many puppies are at the pet store?

Think about what the problem tells you.

There are __5__ cages. There are __4__ puppies in each cage.
What does the problem want you to find?

How many puppies there are at the pet store.

What operation do you need to use? __×__

Circle the number sentence that solves the problem.

(5 × 4 = 20)   5 + 4 = 9   5 − 4 = 1

So, there are __20__ puppies at the pet store.

Write the sign that shows the operation you need to use.
Circle the number sentence that solves the problem.

1. A cage has 9 birds. Jack buys 3 birds.
   How many birds are left?

   What operation do you need to use? ___

   9 + 3 = 12   (9 − 3 = 6)   9 × 3 = 27

   There are __6__ birds left at the pet store.

158   Use with Lesson 12-9.

© Pearson Education, Inc. 2

Name _____

PROBLEM-SOLVING SKILL   P 12-9
Choose an Operation

Circle the number sentence that solves the problem.

1. Sara makes 6 bracelets. She puts 3 beads on each
   bracelet. How many beads does she use in all?

   6 − 3 = 3   6 + 3 = 9   (6 × 3 = 18)

   Sara uses __18__ beads.

2. Monty builds a birdhouse. He uses 7 pieces of wood
   for the house and 3 pieces of wood for the roof.
   How many pieces of wood does he use in all?

   (7 + 3 = 10)   7 × 3 = 21   7 − 3 = 4

   Monty uses __10__ pieces of wood.

3. Mr. Kaplan bakes 8 muffins. He eats 2 muffins
   for breakfast. How many muffins are left?

   8 × 2 = 16   (8 − 2 = 6)   8 + 4 = 12

   Mr. Kaplan has __6__ muffins left.

4. Miss Thomas sews 5 dolls. She has 15 buttons.
   She wants to sew the same number of buttons on
   each doll. How many buttons does each doll get?

   5 + 3 = 8   (15 ÷ 5 = 3)   5 − 3 = 2

   Each doll gets __3__ buttons.

158   Use with Lesson 12-9.

© Pearson Education, Inc. 2

Name _____

PROBLEM-SOLVING APPLICATIONS   R 12-10
Up, Up, and Away!

Write a number sentence.
Decide what operation you
will use to solve the problem.

5 planes are ready for take-off.
There are 3 pilots on each plane.
How many pilots are on the planes altogether?

What numbers will you use? __5__ and __3__

What operation will you use? Write the sign. __×__

__5__ × __3__ = __15__   __15__ pilots are on the planes.

Solve.

1. There are 73 passengers.
   40 of them order chicken for dinner.
   How many passengers do not order chicken?

   __73__ − __40__ = __33__ passengers

2. A plane has 24 seats in one section.
   There are 3 seats in each row.
   How many rows of seats are there?

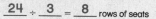

   __24__ ÷ __3__ = __8__ rows of seats

Use with Lesson 12-10.   159

© Pearson Education, Inc. 2

Name _____

PROBLEM-SOLVING APPLICATIONS   P 12-10
Up, Up, and Away!

Solve.

1. A plane has 6 rows of seats in one part of the cabin.
   Each row has 3 seats. How many seats are there in all?

   __6__ rows × __3__ seats in each row = __18__ seats in all

2. Javier brought magazines to read on the plane.
   It took Javier 2 hours to read each magazine.
   The flight lasted 6 hours. How many magazines
   did Javier read during the flight?

   __6__ ÷ __2__ = __3__ magazines

3. A passenger has two suitcases. One suitcase weighs
   27 pounds. The other suitcase weighs 56 pounds.
   How many pounds do the two suitcases weigh in all?

   __27__ + __56__ = __83__ pounds in all

Writing in Math

4. Write a multiplication story about a trip
   you would like to take on an airplane.

   Stories will vary.

   _____

   _____

Use with Lesson 12-10.   159

© Pearson Education, Inc. 2

83